MAKE IT CLEAN & EASY

MAKE IT CLEAN & EASY

YOUR GUIDE TO SKINCARE, BODY-CARE AND CASTILE SOAP FROM SCRATCH

CHRISTINA DENEKA

Flying Sun Press

For my mom Joann, the Platinum Fox,
with love and thanks

CONTENTS

PART TWO

PART THREE

WELCOME

Dear reader,

I am so excited to share this book with you and grateful that our paths are crossing. When you make the shift from consumer to producer, something magical happens. It is extremely empowering when applied to the making of your own clean personal care items. Once you've made some of your own clean items, you will never read an ingredient label the same way again. It is your best defense against *green-washing*, a marketing technique employed by some to make personal care items seem healthy or environmentally friendly despite being anything but.

The goal of this book is to *rocket* you to the top of the learning curve that I scaled over ten years formulating 25,000+ clean personal care items for Hollow Daze Surf

Designs. And I'll guide you there quickly and with almost effortless ease through your basic kitchen skills.

In part one, you will learn all of my signature skincare and body-care formulations. It's like cooking from a recipe, and you will need just your basic kitchen equipment. Then in part two, you will learn how to easily make castile soap from scratch—and without fear—using a dedicated crock-pot and stick blender. Beyond sharing my formulations, in part three, I provide themed production menus that will enable you to create your items with maximum efficiency. Think of it like planning and executing a multi-course meal. You will be astonished at how much you can make in less than five hours, *including* soap. You will also learn how to translate your dreams into reality with your own custom formulations.

If you would like to see the techniques in action, please consider joining me for classes at hollowdazeu.com.

It's all so simple. And I can't wait to show you how.

Much love,
    Christina
    Hatteras Island, Outer Banks, NC

INTRODUCTION

THE MAKE IT CLEAN MANIFESTO

In the context of personal care items, making it clean for me simply means that if I don't want it in my body, I don't use it in my formulations. Wrapped up in that concept is vetting ingredients and suppliers carefully while choosing organic when it makes sense to do so. And if you are making items for others, it also means disclosing your ingredient list in full every time.

Scent vs. Fragrance

Part of making it clean means understanding the important difference between *scent* and *fragrance*. Scent can be clean, depending on what it actually is. For example, essential oils are made from botanicals and are generally considered clean from a scent perspective.

By contrast, fragrance is made from chemicals that can contain thousands of different compounds, including potential carcinogens and endocrine disruptors. I am not aware of any legal distinction among the terms *fragrance, natural fragrance* or *aroma*, and advise against using any such ingredients in your formulations absent a complete ingredient list from the manufacturer that you can verify as clean.

A related important difference is between *essential oil blends* and *fragrance blends containing essential oils*. Essential oil blends are combinations made of essential oils. But fragrance blends containing essential oils are chemical fragrances that also contain essential oils and should be avoided if you want to make it clean.

Some makers do not disclose the essential oils in their formulations, claiming a *proprietary blend* or simply labeling *essential oils*. This is wrong labeling. If you ask the maker and they are unwilling to specify the actual essential oils, take that as a big red flag, particularly if you have allergies or skin sensitivities. And always trust your nose. Some makers incorrectly label fragrance blends that contain essential oils as just *essential oils*.

Color vs. Colorants

Making it clean does not necessarily mean making it colorless, but it does mean avoiding colorants that you wouldn't want in your body. The problem with many soap dyes is that if you drill down into their ingredients, you can find things like parabens and other potentially problematic chemical preservatives.

The good news is that things like herbs, spices, botanicals, and even coffee and tea can be used to provide color (and often functionality) in your creations. There is also potentially room for certain minerals and clays, so long as you know that they come from a clean source and you are comfortable with how they were processed.

Risk Mitigation vs. Preservatives

Making it clean to me means not using any chemical preservatives. Ever. Even in water-based formulations and even though others may differ. The chemicals associated with the preservatives are just more alarming to me than mitigating the risk of contamination when using clean equipment, distilled water, and essential oils that are understood to have antibacterial qualities.

Witch Hazel vs. Alcohol

I use witch hazel, which I think of as nature's alcohol, as the emulsifier in my water-based sprays. Even though others dispute whether you can even achieve emulsification and swear by grain alcohol instead. I simply disagree and find witch hazel formulations gentler and friendlier for sensitive skin.

Solid vs. Pump Lotions

Making it clean usually means making solid beeswax balms or salves, as opposed to the runnier kind of lotion you find in pumps or creams. The reason for this again relates to preservatives. I still have not found any acceptable so-called *natural preservatives*.

If you're really set on making a creamy lotion, you can make it clean, but you'll need to refrigerate, use within a month or so, and pitch if you see any evidence of mold. Alternatively, you can blend a clean, shelf stable oil. This is often the best choice for vegans and those with beeswax or honey sensitivities or allergies.

Salt vs. Sugar Scrubs

When we're talking about the face and body, making it clean for me means choosing salt over sugar for scrubs. With one sticky-sweet exception: lip scrubs. And salt is neither harsh nor painful when you use a fine or very fine grind.

Your Intuition vs. The 'Rules'

You are endowed with the gift of intuition and know your health and skin better than anyone else. Always trust your intuition. Although the information and recipes contained herein is your guide, use your intuition to decide whether any 'rules' should be broken.

PART ONE

ONE

LIP BALM

THESE ARE the only three ingredients you truly need to make a clean lip balm: sunflower oil, beeswax and coconut oil. Other ingredients like alkanet root and kelp can be added for color, along with lip safe essential oils. If you need to source any of the lip balm ingredients, you should be able to find everything you need at Brambleberry, www. brambleberry.com.

Sunflower oil is hands-down the best lip balm ingredient in my experience because it is naturally high in vitamin E, believed to have a natural SPF, and does not make you feel greasy (like grapeseed) or like you need to constantly reapply (like olive oil).

Coconut oil has a lot going for it with your lip skin and I believe it contributes to a very pleasant lip balm texture. But if you used only coconut oil, eventually it is likely that you would experience dryness.

Beeswax is what keeps the lip balm solid. And solid blocks of beeswax are visually stunning. But you must first grate what you need before attempting to melt it. This is why some people, myself included, prefer to work with beeswax pastilles, which come ready to melt in tiny pieces.

Pots vs. Sticks

Pots are generally round and can be made of glass, plastic, metal or other materials. The benefit to using pots is that you can pour your balm directly into them from your glass measuring cup without making a mess, even with the tiny one-fourth ounce glass pots. If size does not matter to you, or you want an XL tub of lip balm, consider using a 4-ounce mason jar for the whole batch.

Sticks are typically plastic twist-ups or paperboard push-ups. When you use plastic sticks, it's best to use a tool to move the balm from your measuring cup into the narrow stick. You can get great results using disposable plastic droppers.

Alternatively, small compostable cups like those for ketchup also work if you fill them about one-third, then gently pinch to form a spout from which to pour. Should you use the ketchup cup method, it is best to allow the cup to rest against the stick as you pour. Expect some messiness until you get the hang of this technique, then it becomes easy.

When you use paperboard push-ups, the opening is wider than that for the plastic sticks, so if you have a steady hand and a light pour, you can try pouring directly into the tube. Ketchup cups also work well for push tubes. Please note, the push up feature of this kind of tube must be properly positioned ahead of time. A skewer makes this very easy.

Packaging

SKS Bottle & Packaging at www.sks-bottle.com is a great source for lip balm containers:

stock number 4036-11 for .25-ounce glass pots,

stock number 0804-08 for .15-ounce black oval plastic sticks,

stock number 8005-05 for .3-ounce brown paperboard push up tube

If you do not wish to purchase packaging in bulk, check out Mountain Rose Herbs at www.mountainroseherbs.com as an alternative.

Microwave vs. Double Boiler

Full disclosure here, I do not generally cook food in a microwave. But I love to use the microwave for making lip balms because it's so easy. You can, however, use a double boiler to avoid the microwave altogether.

Equipment

For all lip balms, you need standard measuring tools: tablespoon, teaspoon, and, if adding a tint, one-half teaspoon.

It is helpful to have a long skewer, but you can also stir with a standard household spoon.

If using the microwave, you also need a two-cup glass measuring cup.

Make clean-up easier by getting as much of the balm as possible into your containers, and then wipe out your measuring cup or double boiler insert before the balm solidifies.

When you are using essential oils, it is generally more precise to work with either glass or plastic droppers as opposed to relying on the orifice reducer present in many essential oil jars. Mountain Rose Herbs is a good source for glass droppers; Wholesale Supplies Plus at www.wholesalesuppliesplus.com is a good source for plastic droppers.

Signature Lip Balm Recipe #1

The yield for this recipe is determined by the size of the containers that you use. You can fill approximately twelve to eighteen lip balm tubes or pots, depending on size. You can simply put the whole batch into a small mason jar and have a big tub of lip balm. I also like to have an extra container on hand for any excess.

Ingredients:

2 tablespoons sunflower oil

1 tablespoon coconut oil

1 tablespoon plus 1 teaspoon beeswax, grated

1. Combine all ingredients in a glass measuring cup and heat in the microwave for two minutes; OR

combine all ingredients in a double boiler insert and heat until melted together and take insert off heat.

2. Stir to combine.

3. Transfer melted balm into containers and let it sit until it has solidified and cooled.

4. Put the covers on the containers.

PRO TIP: if you want a smooth top, fill your container up about seven-eighths to leave some head room. Reserve some of your mixture. After the lip balm has begun to solidify, reheat the reserved portion and use it to top off your container.

Lemongrass Lips

Ingredients:

Signature Recipe

2 tablespoons sunflower oil

1 tablespoon coconut oil

1 tablespoon plus 1 teaspoon beeswax, grated

PLUS

10 drops lemongrass essential oil

1. Combine sunflower oil, coconut oil and beeswax in a glass measuring cup and heat in the microwave for two minutes; OR combine these ingredients in a double boiler insert and heat until melted together and take insert off heat.

2. Stir to combine, then add ten drops lemongrass essential oil and stir again for about thirty seconds.
3. Transfer melted balm into containers and let it sit until it has solidified and cooled.
4. Put the covers on the containers.

Surf Lips

Ingredients:

Signature Recipe

2 tablespoons sunflower oil

1 tablespoon coconut oil

1 tablespoon plus 1 teaspoon beeswax, grated

PLUS

½ teaspoon ground kelp

7 drops lemongrass essential oil

5 drops spearmint essential oil

1. Combine sunflower oil, coconut oil and beeswax in a glass measuring cup and heat in the microwave for two minutes; OR combine these ingredients in a double boiler insert and heat until melted together and take insert off heat.
2. Stir to combine, then add ½ teaspoon kelp and stir again until combined.
3. Add lemongrass and spearmint essential oils and stir again for about thirty seconds.
4. Transfer melted balm into containers and let it sit

until it has solidified and cooled. Let any accumulated kelp remain in the bottom of the measuring cup as you do not need to force it into the containers.

5. Put the covers on the containers.

Lavender Lips

Ingredients:

Signature Recipe

2 tablespoons sunflower oil

1 tablespoon coconut oil

1 tablespoon plus 1 teaspoon beeswax, grated

PLUS

½ teaspoon alkanet root

10 drops lavender essential oil

Optional: a piece of cheese cloth to strain the mixture and an extra glass measuring cup or a compatible second insert for your double boiler, like a glass bowl

1. Combine sunflower oil, coconut oil and beeswax in a glass measuring cup and heat in the microwave for two minutes; OR combine these ingredients in a double boiler insert and heat until melted together and take insert off heat.

2. Stir to combine, then add ½ teaspoon alkanet root and stir again until combined. ONLY IF using optional cheese cloth, position the cloth over the second container and strain the

mixture through it. Reheat for about thirty seconds.

3. Add lavender essential oil and stir again for about thirty seconds.

4. Transfer melted balm into containers and let it sit until it has solidified and cooled. Let any accumulated alkanet root remain in the bottom of the measuring cup as you do not need to force it into the containers.

5. Put the covers on the containers.

PLOT TWIST: if you would like to make this as a lavender lip scrub stick (or pot), add one teaspoon of brown sugar to your mixture after adding the essential oil and stir to combine. Reheat the mixture in twenty-second intervals if it becomes hard to work with; you must move quickly when incorporating sugar.

Lavender & Lemongrass Lips

Ingredients:

Signature Recipe

2 tablespoons sunflower oil

1 tablespoon coconut oil

1 tablespoon plus 1 teaspoon beeswax, grated

PLUS

½ teaspoon alkanet root

5 drops lemongrass essential oil

5 drops lavender essential oil

Optional: a piece of cheese cloth to strain the mixture and an extra glass measuring cup or a compatible second insert for your double boiler, like a glass bowl

1. Combine sunflower oil, coconut oil and beeswax in a glass measuring cup and heat in the microwave for two minutes; OR combine these ingredients in a double boiler insert and heat until melted together and take insert off heat.
2. Stir to combine, then add ½ teaspoon alkanet root and stir again until combined. ONLY IF using optional cheese cloth, position the cloth over the second container and strain the mixture through it. Reheat for about thirty seconds.
3. Add lemongrass and lavender essential oils and stir again for about thirty seconds.
4. Transfer melted balm into containers and let it sit until it has solidified and cooled. Let any accumulated alkanet root remain in the bottom of the measuring cup, you do not need to force it into the containers.
5. Put the covers on the containers.

Lemon Ginger Lips

Ingredients:
Signature Recipe
2 tablespoons sunflower oil
1 tablespoon coconut oil

1 tablespoon plus 1 teaspoon beeswax, grated
PLUS
¼ teaspoon alkanet root
7 drops lemongrass essential oil
5 drops ginger essential oil
Optional: a piece of cheese cloth to strain the mixture and an extra glass measuring cup or a compatible second insert for your double boiler, like a glass bowl.

1. Combine sunflower oil, coconut oil and beeswax in a glass measuring cup and heat in the microwave for two minutes; OR combine these ingredients in a double boiler insert and heat until melted together and take insert off heat.
2. Stir to combine, then add ½ teaspoon alkanet root and stir again until combined. ONLY IF using optional cheese cloth, position the cloth over the second container and strain the mixture through it. Reheat for about thirty seconds.
3. Add lemongrass and ginger essential oils and stir again for about thirty seconds.
4. Transfer melted balm into containers and let it sit until it has solidified and cooled. Let any accumulated alkanet root remain in the bottom of the measuring cup, you do not need to force it into the containers.
5. Put the covers on the containers.

Signature Lip Balm Recipe #2

The yield for this recipe is determined by the size of the containers that you use. You can fill approximately twelve to eighteen lip balm tubes or pots, depending on size. You can simply put the whole batch into a small mason jar and have a big tub of lip balm. I also like to have an extra container on hand for any excess.

Ingredients:

3 tablespoons sunflower oil

1 tablespoon cocoa butter, grated

1 tablespoon plus one teaspoon beeswax, grated

1. Combine all ingredients in a glass measuring cup and heat in the microwave for two minutes; OR combine all ingredients in a double boiler insert and heat until melted together and take insert off heat.
2. Stir to combine.
3. Transfer melted balm into containers and let it sit until it has solidified and cooled.
4. Put the covers on the containers.

PRO TIP: if you want a smooth top, fill your container up about seven-eighths to leave some head room. Reserve some of your mixture. After the lip balm has begun to solidify, reheat the reserved portion and use it to top off your container.

Chocolate Lips

Ingredients:

Signature Recipe
3 tablespoons sunflower oil
1 tablespoon cocoa butter, grated
1 tablespoon plus one teaspoon beeswax, grated
PLUS
½ teaspoon cocoa powder

1. Combine sunflower oil, cocoa butter and beeswax in a glass measuring cup and heat in the microwave for two minutes; OR combine these ingredients in a double boiler insert and heat until melted together and take insert off heat.
2. Stir to combine, then add cocoa powder and stir again for about thirty seconds.
3. Transfer melted balm into containers and let it sit until it has solidified and cooled. Let any accumulated cocoa powder remain in the bottom of the measuring cup, you do not need to force it into the containers.
4. Put the covers on the containers.

Chocolate Peppermint Lips

Ingredients:

Signature Recipe
3 tablespoons sunflower oil

1 tablespoon cocoa butter (grated, pastille or cubed form)

1 tablespoon plus one teaspoon beeswax, grated

PLUS

½ teaspoon alkanet root

8 drops peppermint essential oil

Optional: a piece of cheese cloth to strain the mixture and an extra glass measuring cup or a compatible second insert for your double boiler, like a glass bowl

1. Combine sunflower oil, cocoa butter and beeswax in a glass measuring cup and heat in the microwave for two minutes; OR combine these ingredients in a double boiler insert and heat until melted together and take insert off heat.

2. Stir to combine, then add alkanet root and stir again until combined. ONLY IF using optional cheese cloth, position the cloth over the second container and strain the mixture through it. Reheat for about thirty seconds.

3. Add peppermint essential oil and stir again for about thirty seconds.

4. Transfer melted balm into containers and let it sit until it has solidified and cooled. Let any accumulated alkanet root remain in the bottom of the measuring cup, you do not need to force it into the containers.

5. Put the covers on the containers.

TWO

SHAMAN SUPER STICK AND HEEL CREAM

SHAMAN SUPER STICK was one of my bestselling Hollow Daze Surf Designs products of all time. Customers reported back that it helped with everything from eczema to bug bites. It was even made for a local Children's Museum as a boo-boo stick. Although I sold it primarily in an oval lip balm tube, it is completely okay to package this salve in a glass jar or paperboard push tube of any size.

Please note, when formulating salves containing essential oils, I do not recommend the use of tins for packaging due to possible reactivity.

THE HEEL CREAM is made just like the Super Stick, but with peppermint essential oil as an additional ingredient. That means you can make the Shaman Super Stick recipe, fill a few lip tubes, then add seven drops peppermint essential oil to your mixture, stir thirty seconds, and go on to fill some jars to also make Heel Cream from the same underlying batch.

CUSTOMERS REPORTED BACK that Heel Cream was excellent after a bath or shower to replenish tired feet. Be sure to put on a pair of socks if you're going to walk around before your Heel Cream fully absorbs.

Conversely, I liked to use Heel Cream on my feet ahead of a big day, especially if I was going to be wearing socks inside my shoes. It definitely helped cut down my fatigue factor after full day art shows. Although I sold it primarily in a glass jar, it is completely okay to package this salve in an oval lip balm tube or paperboard push tube of any size.

Remember to always label your creations as the Heel Cream has a bigger kick than the Super Stick.

PACKAGING

SKS Bottle & Packaging at sks-bottle.com is a great source for containers:

stock number 0804-08 for .15-ounce black oval plastic sticks

stock number 8004-02 for a 1-ounce brown paperboard push tube

stock number 8005-04 for a 2-ounce ounce brown paper- board push tube

You can also find nice black or white paperboard push

tubes on Etsy through GreenWay Containers. I really liked their 1.25 ounce push tubes.

For glass jars, SKS has a nice selection of 1 and 2-ounce amber glass jars.

You can find nice blue glass jars at Premium Vials: www. premiumvials.com.

If you do not wish to purchase packaging by the case, check out Mountain Rose Herbs and Etsy as alternatives or use 4-ounce mason jars.

EQUIPMENT

For all salves, a digital kitchen scale is recommended.

It is helpful to have a long skewer, but you can also stir with a standard household spoon.

If using the microwave, you also need a two-cup glass measuring cup.

When you are using essential oils, it is generally more precise to work with either glass or plastic droppers as opposed to relying on the orifice reducer present in many essential oil jars. Mountain Rose Herbs at www. mountainroseherbs.com is a good source for glass droppers; Wholesale Supplies Plus at www.wholesalesuppliesplus.com is a good source for plastic droppers.

Signature Shaman Super Stick Recipe

The yield for this recipe is determined by the size of the containers that you use. You can fill approximately twelve to eighteen lip balm size tubes, depending on size. You can fill approximately four to six larger paperboard tubes, also depending on size. And you can simply put the whole batch into a pint-size mason jar and have a big tub of shaman salve. I also like to have an extra container on hand for any excess.

Ingredients:

2 ½ ounces shea butter

1 $^5/_8$ ounces avocado oil

1 ounce beeswax

$^1/_8$ ounce meadowfoam seed oil (optional)

10 drops lavender essential oil

10 drops tea tree essential oil

10 drops rosemary essential oil

1. Combine avocado oil, shea butter and beeswax in a glass measuring cup and heat in the microwave for two minutes; OR combine these ingredients in a double boiler insert and heat until melted together and take insert off heat.

2. Stir to combine, then add meadowfoam seed oil if using and stir again for thirty seconds. Add lavender, tea tree and rosemary essential oils and stir again thirty seconds.

3. Transfer salve into containers of your choice and let it sit until it has solidified and cooled.

4. Put the covers on the containers.

PRO TIP: if you want a smooth top, fill your container up about seven-eighths to leave some head room. Reserve some of your mixture. After the salve has begun to solidify, reheat the reserved portion and use it to top off your container.

Shaman Heel Cream

Ingredients:
    Signature Shaman Super Stick Recipe
    2 ½ ounces shea butter
    1 ⅝ ounces avocado oil
    1 ounce beeswax
    ⅛ ounce meadowfoam seed oil (optional to make the salve smoother)
    10 drops lavender essential oil
    10 drops tea tree essential oil
    10 drops rosemary essential oil
    PLUS
    10 drops peppermint essential oil

1. Combine avocado oil, shea butter and beeswax in a glass measuring cup and heat in the microwave for two minutes; OR combine these ingredients in a double boiler insert and heat until melted together and take insert off heat.
2. Stir to combine, then add meadowfoam seed oil if using and stir again for thirty seconds. Add lavender, tea tree, rosemary and peppermint essential oils and stir again thirty seconds.
3. Transfer salve into containers of your choice and let it sit until it has solidified and cooled.

4. Put the covers on the containers.

Frankincense Facial Stick

Follow the Signature Shaman Super Stick Recipe, but use these essential oils instead:

15 drops lavender essential oil

15 drops frankincense essential oil (*Boswellia carteri*)

15 drops myrrh essential oil (I like the myrrh from Mountain Rose Herbs)

THREE

DEODORANT

THIS CHAPTER COULD BE a book in itself with all of the experiments I have made over the years in pursuit of a good clean deodorant formulation. Ultimately, I concluded that the combination of shea butter, coconut oil and beeswax with meadowfoam seed oil, baking soda and tea tree essential oil worked best.

I know that some people cannot use baking soda because they experience uncomfortable pit rash. If you cannot use baking soda, try substituting arrowroot powder. In my experience, it is more gentle and works okay. I have also tried diatomaceous earth as a substitute—with disastrous results.

I also found that with some of my older customers, cocoa butter was more comfortable for them than shea butter, which can be stiffer to apply. If you are formulating for mature pits, consider substituting cocoa butter.

If you are super sensitive, try adjusting the shea butter

and beeswax down one-eighth ounce and upping the coconut oil by one-quarter ounce for a different, somewhat softer consistency. The more beeswax, the 'stiffer' the formulation.

If you still cannot use a solid, you might consider making the magnesium oil spray. I tested a lot of spray concepts to try to get out of using a stick. Witch hazel was a hilarious epic fail. But the magnesium oil held promise, so I am including it.

Whatever you do, please avoid using lemongrass essential oil in any of your deodorant formulations. I have found that it has a tendency to cause underarm irritation.

Packaging

All deodorant packaging kind of stinks. The usual plastic twist-up tube is okay, but if you crank it up too high, it can get messy when the lid goes back on. This is also true with paperboard, but to a lesser extent. I am now firmly in the camp of preferring the 1.25-ounce paperboard push tubes that you can get on Etsy from GreenWay Containers.

SKS Bottle & Packaging at www.sks-bottle.com is another good source for deodorant containers.

stock number 0804-11 for 2.65-ounce black oval tubes

stock number 8005-04 for a 2-ounce brown paperboard push tube

If you don't mind using your fingers to apply as a pit paste, a 4-ounce mason jar makes a fine deodorant vessel.

Equipment

For deodorant, a digital kitchen scale is recommended.

It is helpful to have a long skewer, but you can also stir with a standard household spoon.

You will need a glass measuring cup for the baking soda and, if using the microwave, you also need an additional two-cup glass measuring cup.

When you are using essential oils, it is generally more precise to work with either glass or plastic droppers as opposed to relying on the orifice reducer present in many essential oil jars. Mountain Rose Herbs at www.mountainroseherbs.com is a good source for glass droppers; Wholesale Supplies Plus at www.wholesalesuppliesplus.com is a good source for plastic droppers.

Signature Shaman Deodorant Recipe

The yield for this recipe is determined by the size of the containers that you use. You can fill approximately three traditional plastic deodorant containers, or about six large paperboard tubes, depending on size . You can also put the whole batch into a pint-size mason jar and have a big tub of deodorant if you don't mind applying it with your fingers. Be sure to have an extra container on hand in case of any excess.

Ingredients:

1 ½ ounces shea butter

1 ½ ounces coconut oil

1 ½ ounces beeswax

8 drops meadowfoam seed oil (optional but it makes the application smoother)

8 drops tea tree essential oil

4 ounces sodium bicarbonate (aka baking soda)

1. Measure out your baking soda in a separate container and set aside.

2. Combine shea butter, coconut oil and beeswax in a glass measuring cup and heat in the microwave for two minutes; OR combine these ingredients in a double boiler insert and heat until melted together and take insert off heat.

3. Stir to combine, then add meadowfoam seed oil if using and stir again for 30 seconds. Add tea tree essential oil and stir again for about thirty seconds.

4. Add the baking soda to the mix while stirring constantly; my favorite stirring tool in this case is a smooth butter knife or spreader. If it starts to get too thick, reheat in thirty-second increments in the microwave or return to the double boiler until it is back to a pourable consistency.

5. Transfer deodorant into containers of your choice and let it sit until it has solidified and cooled.

6. Put the covers on the containers.

PRO TIP: if you want a smooth top, fill your container up about seven-eighths to leave some head room. Reserve enough deodorant to reheat it and pour it over the top after the bottom part has begun to solidify.

Rose Geranium

This is the strongest odor killing natural deodorant that I've ever made, originally as a custom request for someone who said natural deodorant never worked for her. I was extremely gratified to hear back that this one worked! It has to do with the characteristics of the essential oils working together.

Ingredients:

Signature Shaman Deodorant Recipe, with different essential oil content

1 ½ ounces shea butter

1 ½ ounces coconut oil

1 ½ ounces beeswax

8 drops meadowfoam seed oil (optional but it makes the application smoother)

4 ounces sodium bicarbonate (aka baking soda)

PLUS

10 drops lavender essential oil

5 drops tea tree essential oil

5 drops rosemary essential oil

10 drops rose geranium essential oil

8 drops ylang ylang essential oil

Patchouli Sandalwood

This was my most-requested custom deodorant formulation so I added it to the line for 2020.

Ingredients:

Signature Shaman Deodorant Recipe, with different essential oil content

1 ½ ounces shea butter

1 ½ ounces coconut oil

1 ½ ounces beeswax

8 drops meadowfoam seed oil (optional but it makes the application smoother)

4 ounces sodium bicarbonate (aka baking soda)

PLUS

20 drops patchouli essential oil

5 drops sandalwood essential oil

10 drops tea tree essential oil

Palo Santo

This is my personal all time favorite deodorant.

Ingredients:

Signature Shaman Deodorant Recipe, with different essential oil content

1 ½ ounces shea butter

1 ½ ounces coconut oil

1 ½ ounces beeswax

8 drops meadowfoam seed oil (optional but it makes the application smoother)

4 ounces sodium bicarbonate (aka baking soda)
PLUS
10 drops palo santo essential oil
20 drops frankincense essential oil
10 drops vetiver essential oil

Packaging Spray Deodorant

Both the container and the sprayer are important in choosing packaging for magnesium oil spray as a deodorant alternative. My favorite spray containers are colored glass because they protect the essential oils yet you can still see how much you are pouring. For sprayers, I strongly prefer those sold as "fine mist."

SKS Bottle & Packaging at www.sks-bottle.com is a good source for fine mist sprayers.

stock number 4003-24 for 2-ounce blue glass bottle with fine mist sprayer

stock number 4001-47 for 2-ounce brown glass bottle with fine mist sprayer

If you do not wish to purchase packaging by the case, check out Mountain Rose Herbs as an alternative.

Signature Magnesium Oil Spray Recipe

Some people experience a stinging sensation when applying this spray, which can signify a possible magnesium deficiency. For magnesium supplementation (as opposed to deodorant)

shoot for ten-to-twenty sprays per day on arms, legs and stomach.

This recipe makes two 2-ounce sprays.

Ingredients:

¼ cup magnesium chloride flakes

¼ cup distilled water

10 drops tea tree essential oil

1. Place the magnesium chloride flakes in a glass two-cup measure.
2. Boil the distilled water, then pour it over the flakes until they are completely dissolved.
3. Let the mixture cool, then add tea tree essential oil and stir for about ninety seconds.
4. Pour into a glass spray bottle.

Lavender

Follow the Signature recipe, but reduce the tea tree essential oil to four drops and also add six drops of lavender essential oil.

Peppermint

Follow the Signature recipe, but reduce the tea tree essential oil to four drops and also add six drops of peppermint essential oil.

Woodsy

Follow the Signature recipe, but substitute six drops patchouli essential oil and four drops vetiver essential oil for the tea tree essential oil.

Fresh

Follow the Signature recipe, but substitute four drops orange essential oil, four drops vetiver essential oil and four drops lavender essential oil for the tea tree essential oil.

FOUR

SPRAYS

I LOVE SPRAYS. They are a great way to test out essential oil combinations and can be used flexibly—for the body, room or linens. Always use distilled water when making sprays. Also, consider using a funnel, it makes life much easier. Witch hazel is my go-to emulsifier, even though opinions are mixed on the subject. I especially like the organic witch hazel available Mountain Rose Herbs. Both Brambleberry and Bulk Apothecary also sell conventional witch hazel that I have used with success.

Remember, if you are doing a body spray and using true citrus essential oil, there is a risk of photosensitization so you should not head right out into the blazing sun.

Packaging

Both the container and the sprayer are important in choosing spray packaging. My favorite spray containers are colored glass because they protect the essential oils yet you can still see how much you are pouring. I have also used opaque containers but then it is best to use a scale so that you do not overfill the container. For sprayers, I strongly prefer those sold as "fine mist." But I have also purchased standard sprayers if I was in love with a particular glass bottle.

SKS Bottle & Packaging at www.sks-bottle.com is a good source for fine mist sprayers.

stock number 4003-24 for 2-ounce blue glass bottle with fine mist sprayer

stock number 4001-47 for 2-ounce brown glass bottle with fine mist sprayer

stock number 5400-02 for 80ml aluminum bottle with fine mist sprayer and stock number 5400- 09 for the XL size (note: back when I used these bottles, there was information about the interior coating that I no longer see on the website. At the time, I was satisfied it would not react with the essential oils. Because things change, if you are in love with these bottles, consider checking with the manufacturer to make sure it satisfies your clean criteria).

I also liked the different colorful glass bottles in a 1-ounce (but not the sprayers as much) from www.containerandpackagingsupply.com.

If you do not wish to purchase packaging by the case, check out Mountain Rose Herbs as an alternative.

Equipment

For all sprays, a digital kitchen scale and a funnel are recommended.

It is helpful to have a long skewer, but you can also stir with a standard household spoon.

You will also need a two-cup glass measuring cup.

When you are using essential oils, it is generally more precise to work with either glass or plastic droppers as opposed to relying on the orifice reducer present in many essential oil jars. Mountain Rose Herbs at www.mountainroseherbs.com is a good source for glass droppers; Wholesale Supplies Plus at www.wholesalesuppliesplus.com is a good source for plastic droppers.

Signature Recipe #1: Lighthouse Lemongrass

This is the recipe for my bestselling bug spray to help with mosquitoes and ticks. Shake before applying and remember to spray not just yourself, but your clothes and gear. I also like to spray the floorboards of my vehicle. For best results, try to apply before leaving the house and getting sweaty.

Here in coastal North Carolina, the bugs have special powers after dark. My rule is if there's no breeze I try to stay inside at nighttime. Otherwise consider wearing lightweight long sleeves and pants, spray your clothes thoroughly and be sure to catch the breezes. If you get bit up, the Shaman Super Stick and Heel Cream help take away the irritation and speed healing. And if you are a true bug magnet, consider making the companion Lighthouse Lemongrass soap.

This recipe is for a 2-ounce spray. You can simply quadruple everything to make an XL 8 ounce spray.

Ingredients:

1 ounce witch hazel

1 ounce distilled water

12 drops lemongrass essential oil

6 drops tea tree essential oil

1. Weigh out your witch hazel and distilled water into your glass two cup measure and stir to combine.
2. Pour the solution into your spray bottle, using a funnel if desired.
3. Add the essential oils.
4. Cap the bottle and shake to combine, about sixty seconds.

Manns Harbor Fly Spray

This one helps with the green flies that like to visit Manns Harbor in the summertime.

Follow the Signature recipe and add six drops lavender essential oil along with the other oils.

Beach Fly Spray

This one helps with the black flies that visit the beaches of the Outer Banks for a few weeks in the summertime.

Ingredients:

Signature recipe, with different essential oils

1 ounce witch hazel

1 ounce distilled water

PLUS

6 drops peppermint essential oil

6 drops rosemary essential oil

6 drops tulsi essential oil (*Ocimum sanctum L.; synonym of Ocimum tenuiflorum L.*)

Pointe Spray

I made this to help with a wonderful dancer's not so wonderful smelly pointe shoes. Note, this was specifically designed for use on the shoes, not for use on human skin as it is strong and could be irritating.

Ingredients:

Signature recipe, with different essential oils

1 ounce witch hazel

1 ounce distilled water

PLUS

12 drops peppermint essential oil

8 drops tea tree essential oil

6 drops eucalyptus essential oil

4 drops sweet basil essential oil (*Ocimum basilicum*)

Signature Recipe #2: Surf Spray

This is the after sun spray to cool and soothe. In the hottest months, it's divine to chill Surf Spray in your fridge or cooler, although you do not have to do so. Supply wise, I like the thin aloe vera gel from Mountain Rose Herbs.

This recipe is for a 2-ounce spray. You can simply quadruple everything to make an XL 8 ounce spray.

Ingredients:

¼ ounce witch hazel

¼ ounce aloe vera

1 ½ ounce distilled water

6 drops peppermint essential oil

3 drops lavender essential oil

1. Weigh out your witch hazel, aloe and distilled water into your glass two-cup measure and whisk thoroughly to combine.
2. Pour the solution into your spray bottle, using a funnel if desired.
3. Add the essential oils.
4. Cap the bottle and shake to combine, about sixty seconds.

PRO TIP: prolong your aloe vera's shelf life with refrigeration for long-term storage.

Signature Recipe #3: Aroma Spray

Here is the base formulation to use for your body, room and linen sprays. Please note, however, that if you make a spray with a dark, heavy essential oil like patchouli, those are best for the body and/or room as opposed to linens due to the possibility of staining.

This recipe is for a 2-ounce spray. You can simply quadruple everything to make an XL 8 ounce spray.

Ingredients:

¼ ounce witch hazel

1 ¾ ounces distilled water

1. Weigh out your witch hazel and distilled water into your glass two-cup measure and whisk thoroughly to combine.
2. Pour the solution into your spray bottle, using a funnel if desired.
3. Add the essential oils (see variations below).
4. Cap the bottle and shake to combine, about sixty seconds.

PRO TIP: to make aroma sprays in bulk, pour off sixteen ounces from a fresh gallon of distilled water. Reserve for another use (like soap, as many recipes call for exactly sixteen ounces of distilled water). Then add sixteen ounces witch hazel to your distilled water. Replace the cap and, while holding it firmly in place, invert and shake to combine.

Chai

A clean alternative to scent your room for fall and the holiday season.

Ingredients:

Signature recipe

¼ ounce witch hazel

1 ¾ ounces distilled water

PLUS

8 drops orange essential oil

5 drops clove essential oil

3 drops ginger essential oil

5 drops tangerine essential oil

NOTE: this is best as a room spray and only an occasional body spray as the clove essential oil is very strong and can bio-accumulate if used to excess for your particular body chemistry.

Cindy's Dream

Ingredients:

Signature recipe

¼ ounce witch hazel

1 ¾ ounces distilled water

PLUS

12 drops sandalwood essential oil

10 drops ylang ylang essential oil

5 drops bergamot essential oil

4 drops tangerine essential oil

3 drops clary sage essential oil

Dream

This is the spray that tends to put people into a good mood, particularly when going through the ups and downs of the menstrual cycle, and is also lovely in the hair.

Ingredients:

Signature recipe

¼ ounce witch hazel

1 ¾ ounces distilled water

PLUS

10 drops ylang ylang essential oil

5 drops bergamot essential oil

4 drops tangerine essential oil

3 drops clary sage essential oil

Equinox

A wonderful travel spray that is energizing and anti-bacterial.

Ingredients:

Signature recipe

¼ ounce witch hazel

1 ¾ ounces distilled water

PLUS

9 drops orange essential oil

6 drops tangerine essential oil

3 drops spearmint essential oil

2 drops tea tree essential oil

Lavender

A very popular body, room and linen spray.

Ingredients:

Signature recipe

¼ ounce witch hazel

1 ¾ ounces distilled water

PLUS

11 drops lavender essential oil

2 drops clary sage essential oil

Lavender Dream

This spray is excellent at bedtime, particularly with children.

Ingredients:

Signature recipe

¼ ounce witch hazel

1 ¾ ounces distilled water

PLUS

10 drops lavender essential oil

10 drops ylang ylang essential oil

5 drops bergamot essential oil

4 drops tangerine essential oil

3 drops clary sage essential oil

Lavender Lemongrass

The classic combination.

Ingredients:

Signature recipe

¼ ounce witch hazel

1 ¾ ounces distilled water

PLUS

10 drops lavender essential oil

1 drop clary sage essential oil

3 drops lemongrass essential oil

Lemon Ginger

This is the spray that some particularly liked on achy joints.

Ingredients:

Signature recipe

¼ ounce witch hazel

1 ¾ ounces distilled water

PLUS

9 drops lemongrass essential oil

9 drops ginger essential oil

Neroli Ravensara

Ingredients:

Signature recipe

¼ ounce witch hazel

1 ¾ ounces distilled water

PLUS

18 drops ravensara essential oil

18 drops neroli essential oil (organic 10% from Eden

Botanicals, which means this also contains coconut oil as an ingredient)

Orange Clove Spray

Ingredients:
  Signature recipe
  ¼ ounce witch hazel
  1 ¾ ounces distilled water
  PLUS
  8 drops orange essential oil
  5 drops clove essential oil
  3 drops fennel essential oil
  2 drops clary sage essential oil
NOTE: this is best as a room spray and only an occasional body spray as the clove essential oil is very strong and can bio-accumulate if used to excess for your particular body chemistry.

Palo Santo

My favorite spray from our Energetics line, this one is all about positive energy. I liked to source the palo santo and vetiver (India) essential oils from Eden Botanicals at www.edenbotanicals.com and the frankincense from either Mountain Rose Herbs or Brambleberry.
  Ingredients:
  Signature recipe
  ¼ ounce witch hazel

1 ¾ ounces distilled water
PLUS
8 drops palo santo essential oil
8 drops vetiver essential oil
10 drops frankincense essential oil (*Boswellia carteri*)

Patchouli Sandalwood

When sourcing sandalwood essential oil, I highly recommend treating yourself to all of the samples from Eden Botanicals and choosing your favorite. Alternatively, the standard Australian sandalwood essential oils from both Brambleberry and Bulk Apothecary are also good.

Ingredients:
Signature recipe
¼ ounce witch hazel
1 ¾ ounces distilled water
PLUS
8 drops patchouli essential oil
5 drops sandalwood essential oil
3 drops ylang ylang essential oil
2 drops clary sage essential oil

Patchulio

The delightful combination of patchouli and orange.
Ingredients:
Signature recipe
¼ ounce witch hazel

1 ¾ ounces distilled water

PLUS

10 drops lavender essential oil

4 drops orange essential oil

2 drops rosemary essential oil

10 drops patchouli essential oil

2 drops clary sage essential oil

Rose Geranium

This one is great for self-care.

Ingredients:

Signature recipe

¼ ounce witch hazel

1 ¾ ounces distilled water

PLUS

10 drops rose geranium essential oil

10 drops ylang ylang essential oil

9 drops rose otto essential oil (Bulgaria 5% from Eden Botanicals, which means this also contains coconut oil as an ingredient)

White Sage

A smokeless alternative to smudging, this spray is great for energy clearing. I particularly like the white sage essential oil from Eden Botanicals at www.edenbotanicals.com.

Ingredients:

Signature recipe

¼ ounce witch hazel

1 ¾ ounces distilled water

PLUS

11 drops sage essential oil (*Salvia officinalis*)

6 drops rosemary essential oil

6 drops lemon essential oil

3 drops white sage essential oil (*Salvia apiana*)

Grief

I make this for friends and family when appropriate.

Ingredients:

Signature recipe

¼ ounce witch hazel

1 ¾ ounces distilled water

PLUS

4 drops cypress essential oil

4 drops clary sage essential oil

4 drops frankincense essential oil

4 drops lavender essential oil

2 drops sandalwood essential oil

3 drops tangerine essential oil

Refresh Room Spray

This is the bathroom spray that at one time was called No. 2 Spray.

Ingredients:

Signature recipe

¼ ounce witch hazel

1 ¾ ounces distilled water

PLUS

6 drops lemongrass essential oil

6 drops grapefruit essential oil

6 drops orange essential oil

4 drops eucalyptus essential oil

FIVE

TONERS

WITCH HAZEL TONERS are gently astringent, meaning they can help reduce excess oil and manage your complexion. They are sprayed onto the skin, typically after washing your face or taking a shower, and then left to evaporate.

Packaging

Both the container and the sprayer are important in choosing spray packaging. My favorite spray containers are colored glass because they protect the essential oils yet you can still see how much you are pouring. For sprayers, I strongly prefer those sold as "fine mist."

SKS Bottle & Packaging at www.sks-bottle.com is a good source for fine mist sprayers.

stock number 4003-24 for 2-ounce blue glass bottle with fine mist sprayer

stock number 4001-47 for 2-ounce brown glass bottle with fine mist sprayer

If you do not wish to purchase packaging by the case, check out Mountain Rose Herbs as an alternative.

Equipment

For all toners, a digital kitchen scale and a funnel are recommended.

When you are using essential oils, it is generally more precise to work with either glass or plastic droppers as opposed to relying on the orifice reducer present in many essential oil jars. Mountain Rose Herbs at www. mountainroseherbs.com is a good source for glass droppers; Wholesale Supplies Plus at www.wholesalesuppliesplus.com is a good source for plastic droppers.

Signature Recipe #1: Shaman Facial Toner

This is the toner that was preferred by those with acne prone skin.

This recipe is for a 2-ounce toner.

Ingredients:

2 ounces witch hazel

12 drops lavender essential oil

12 drops tea tree essential oil

1. Using your digital scale, weigh out your witch

hazel directly into your glass bottle ideally using a funnel.
2. Add the essential oils.
3. Cap the bottle and shake to combine, about sixty seconds.

Signature Recipe #2: Frankincense Facial Toner

This toner delivers a lot of support, particularly for mature skin. I particularly like the myrrh essential oil from Mountain Rose Herbs.

This recipe is for a 2-ounce toner.

Ingredients:

2 ounces witch hazel

10 drops lavender essential oil

10 drops tea tree essential oil

5 drops ylang ylang essential oil

6 drops frankincense essential oil (*Boswellia carteri*)

3 drops myrrh essential oil

10 drops jojoba essential oil

1. Using your digital scale, weigh out your witch hazel directly into your glass bottle ideally using a funnel.
2. Add the essential oils.
3. Cap the bottle and shake to combine, about sixty seconds.

SIX

FACIAL MISTS

MILDER THAN A WITCH HAZEL TONER, facial mists are made from hydrosols. My favorite hydrosols come from Eden Botanicals at www.edenbotanicals.com where you can read all about them. I highly recommend treating yourself to their sampler.

Packaging

Both the container and the sprayer are important in choosing spray packaging. My favorite spray containers are colored glass because they protect the essential oils yet you can still see how much you are pouring. For sprayers, I strongly prefer those sold as "fine mist."

SKS Bottle & Packaging at www.sks-bottle.com is a good source for fine mist sprayers.

stock number 4003-24 for 2-ounce blue glass bottle with fine mist sprayer

stock number 4001-47 for 2-ounce brown glass bottle with fine mist sprayer

If you do not wish to purchase packaging by the case, check out Mountain Rose Herbs as an alternative.

Equipment

For all mists, a digital kitchen scale and a funnel are recommended.

For the Cucumber Facial Mist, it is helpful to have a long skewer, but you can also stir with a standard household spoon and you will need a glass measuring cup.

When you are using essential oils, it is generally more precise to work with either glass or plastic droppers as opposed to relying on the orifice reducer present in many essential oil jars. Mountain Rose Herbs at www.mountain-roseherbs.com is a good source for glass droppers; Wholesale Supplies Plus at www.wholesalesuppliesplus.com is a good source for plastic droppers.

Signature Recipe #1: Rose Facial Mist

This recipe is for a 2-ounce spray. When I was making these, I sourced all of the ingredients from Eden Botanicals.

Ingredients:

2 ounces organic rose hydrosol

12 drops rose otto essential oil (Bulgaria 5%, which means this also contains coconut oil as an ingredient)

12 drops neroli essential oil (organic 10%, which means this also contains coconut oil as an ingredient)

1. Using your digital scale, weigh out your rose hydrosol directly into your glass bottle ideally using a funnel.
2. Add the essential oils.
3. Cap the bottle and shake to combine, about sixty seconds.

PRO TIP: refrigerate your hydrosols for long-term storage.

Signature Recipe #2: Cucumber Facial Mist

This recipe is for a 2-ounce spray. When I was making these, I sourced the cucumber hydrosol from Eden Botanicals. My preferred aloe vera is from Mountain Rose Herbs.

Ingredients:

1 ½ ounce cucumber hydrosol

¼ ounce aloe vera

¼ ounce witch hazel

2 drops peppermint essential oil

10 drops lavender essential oil

1. Using your digital scale, weigh out your cucumber hydrosol into your glass measuring cup ideally using a funnel.

2. Add the aloe vera and whisk to combine.
3. Transfer the mixture to the bottle using a funnel.
4. Add the essential oils.
5. Cap the bottle and shake to combine, about sixty seconds.

SEVEN

SERUM AND OILS

CLEAN SERUMS and oils consist of oil blends to support your skin and are a great substitute for conventional moisturizers. The primary difference for is that serums tend to be heavier and slower to absorb whereas oils tend to be more lightweight and typically absorb faster.

Packaging

Depending on personal preference, you can package serums and oils in glass jars with either fine mist sprayers or treatment pumps.

SKS Bottle & Packaging at www.sks-bottle.com is a good source for fine mist sprayers and treatment pumps:

stock number 4003-24 for 2-ounce blue glass bottle with fine mist sprayer

stock number 4001-47 for 2-ounce brown glass bottle with fine mist sprayer

stock number 4003-62 for 2-ounce blue glass bottle with treatment pump

stock number 4001-72 for amber glass bottle with treatment pump

If you do not wish to purchase packaging by the case, check out Mountain Rose Herbs as an alternative.

Equipment

For serums and oils, a digital kitchen scale and a funnel are recommended.

It is helpful to have a long skewer, but you can also stir with a standard household spoon.

When you are using essential oils, it is generally more precise to work with either glass or plastic droppers as opposed to relying on the orifice reducer present in many essential oil jars. Mountain Rose Herbs at www.mountainroseherbs.com is a good source for glass droppers; Wholesale Supplies Plus at www.wholesalesuppliesplus.com is a good source for plastic droppers.

Signature Recipe #1: Nourish Serum

This slow absorbing blend is a clean, stable alternative to moisturizer. This recipe is for a 2-ounce bottle.

Ingredients:

1 $^3/_8$ ounces extra virgin olive oil

$1/2$ ounce sunflower oil

$1/_8$ ounce apricot kernel oil

8 drops jojoba

1. Weigh out the oils into your glass measuring cup.
2. Add the jojoba and stir to combine.
3. Transfer the mixture to the bottle using a funnel.
4. Cap the bottle and shake to combine, about sixty seconds.

Frankincense Facial Serum

This was my bestselling skincare product of all time. I am happy to share it with you now. It worked wonders for many of my customers with mature or sensitive skin, and the best part was there's no need to make compromises with chemical ingredients. Many people like to use this about thirty minutes before bedtime to allow time to absorb.

This recipe is for a 2-ounce bottle.

Ingredients:

$1 \, ^3/_8$ ounces extra virgin olive oil

$1/2$ ounce sunflower oil

$1/_8$ ounce apricot kernel oil

8 drops jojoba

7 drops lavender essential oil

2 drops tea tree essential oil

3 drops ylang ylang essential oil

6 drops frankincense essential oil (*Boswellia carteri*)

3 drops myrrh essential oil

1. Weigh out the olive, sunflower and apricot kernel oils into your glass measuring cup.
2. Add the jojoba and stir to combine.
3. Transfer the mixture to the bottle using a funnel.
4. Add the essential oils.
5. Cap the bottle and shake to combine, about sixty seconds.

Signature Recipe #2: Scalp Serum

I custom blended this scalp serum and received very positive feedback. Dispense into your hands and apply just a little at a time with your fingers.

This recipe is for a 2-ounce bottle.

Ingredients:

1 ½ ounces castor oil

½ ounce jojoba

8 drops rosemary essential oil

8 drops lavender essential oil

5 drops cedarwood essential oil (optional)

1. Weigh out the castor oil and jojoba in your glass measuring cup.
2. Whisk to combine.
3. Transfer the mixture to the bottle using a funnel.
4. Add the essential oils.
5. Cap the bottle and shake to combine, about sixty seconds.

Signature Recipe #3: Coffee Eye Serum

This was another custom request because many products that target under-eye puffiness contain ingredients that are not considered clean. I packaged this in a glass jar with a reducer cap. It does not do what some of the chemicals do, but helped a bit. Using the ring finger, apply just a drop or two under the eye, taking care never to get it in your eye.

Ingredients:

¼ ounce argan oil

10 drops frankincense essential oil (*Boswellia carteri*)

6 drops coffee CO_2 extract (from Eden Botanicals)

Simply combine all ingredients in a 10ml glass jar, affix the orifice reducer and shake to combine sixty seconds. You can get these jars from Mountain Rose Herbs, or in bulk from SKS.

Signature Recipe #4: Sheer Oil

This is the master blend for my sheer, relatively quick absorbing oil formulations.

This recipe is for a 2-ounce bottle.

Ingredients:

1 ¹/₈ ounces grapeseed oil

½ ounce olive oil

¹/₈ ounce sunflower oil

¹/₈ ounce rice bran oil

6 drops jojoba

1. Weigh out the grapeseed, olive, sunflower and rice bran oils into your glass measuring cup.
2. Add the jojoba and stir to combine.
3. Transfer the mixture to the bottle using a funnel.
4. Cap the bottle and shake to combine, about sixty seconds.

Frankincense Body & Facial Oil

This formulation had a devoted following, particularly among those who wanted to incorporate frankincense and myrrh into their skincare routine without much additional scent.

This recipe is for a 2-ounce bottle.

Ingredients:

$1 \, ^1/_8$ ounces grapeseed oil

½ ounce olive oil

$^1/_8$ ounce sunflower oil

$^1/_8$ ounce rice bran oil

6 drops jojoba

6 drops frankincense essential oil (*Boswellia carteri*)

3 drops myrrh essential oil

1. Weigh out the grapeseed, olive, sunflower and rice bran oils into your glass measuring cup.
2. Add the jojoba and stir to combine.
3. Transfer the mixture to the bottle using a funnel.
4. Add the essential oils.
5. Cap the bottle and shake to combine, about sixty seconds.

Shaman Facial Oil

This formulation was popular as a moisturizer alternative for acne prone customers.

This recipe is for a 2-ounce bottle.

Ingredients:

1 $^1/_8$ ounces grapeseed oil

½ ounce olive oil

$^1/_8$ ounce sunflower oil

$^1/_8$ ounce rice bran oil

6 drops jojoba

12 drops lavender essential oil

12 drops tea tree essential oil

1. Weigh out the grapeseed, olive, sunflower and rice bran oils into your glass measuring cup.
2. Add the jojoba and stir to combine.
3. Transfer the mixture to the bottle using a funnel.
4. Add the essential oils.
5. Cap the bottle and shake to combine, about sixty seconds.

Shaman Body & Leg Oil

A very popular formulation to help legs feel soft but look toned. I also had a report from the mountains of Georgia that it worked great to help deter chiggers.

This recipe is for a 2-ounce bottle.

Ingredients:

1 $^1/_8$ ounces grapeseed oil

½ ounce olive oil

$^1/_8$ ounce sunflower oil

$^1/_8$ ounce rice bran oil

6 drops jojoba

6 drops lavender essential oil

6 drops peppermint essential oil

2 drops clary sage essential oil

1. Weigh out the grapeseed, olive, sunflower and rice bran oils into your glass measuring cup.
2. Add the jojoba and stir to combine.
3. Transfer the mixture to the bottle using a funnel.
4. Add the essential oils.
5. Cap the bottle and shake to combine, about sixty seconds.

Cindy's Dream

This is a custom recipe for an approximately 8-ounce bottle of sheer oil, and typically yielded a little extra. Most of my blends have just five or fewer essential oils, but this one evolved over time and broke the 'rules' in a good way.

Ingredients:

4 ½ ounces grapeseed oil

3 ounces olive oil

½ ounce sunflower oil

½ ounce rice bran oil

30 drops jojoba oil

20 drops ylang ylang essential oil

5 drops tangerine essential oil

5 drops bergamot essential oil

5 to 20 drops clary sage essential oil

5 to 40 drops sandalwood essential oil

5 drops frankincense essential oil (*Boswellia carteri*)

5 drops rose otto essential oil

1. Weigh out the grapeseed, olive, sunflower and rice bran oils into your glass measuring cup.
2. Add the jojoba and stir to combine.
3. Add the essential oils and stir sixty seconds to combine.
4. Transfer the mixture to the XL bottle using a funnel.
5. Cap the bottle, invert, then return to upright position.

Signature Recipe #5: Bath Drops

If you are going to use essential oils in the tub, it is best to formulate them in a carrier beforehand to avoid essential oils going directly into the skin and potentially causing irritation. I called these bath drops because I used a tube with a dropper lid for packaging. But you can use a spray bottle or treatment pump to dispense the equivalent of just a few drops into your tub, stirring thoroughly before you enter the tub.

Ingredients:

1 ¾ ounces fractionated coconut oil

½ ounce argan oil

75 drops lavender essential oil OR 25 drops lemongrass essential oil and 50 drops ginger essential oil

1. Weigh out the fractionated coconut and argan oil into your glass measuring cup.
2. Add the jojoba and stir to combine.
3. Add the essential oils and whisk ninety seconds to combine.
4. Transfer the mixture to your desired container using a funnel.

EIGHT

ROLLERS

I LOVE ROLLERS. They are super convenient and generally travel well. You can purchase small quantities of roll top glass bottles through Mountain Rose Herbs. Another place to find glass rollers in amber, blue or green glass with stainless steel balls is amazon.com.

All of these recipes are for 10ml rollers.

Equipment

For all rollers, a digital kitchen scale is recommended.

It is helpful to have a long skewer, but you can also stir with a standard household spoon.

I recommend using a pint-sized mason jar instead of a glass measuring cup for rollers.

When you are using essential oils, it is generally more precise to work with either glass or plastic droppers as opposed to relying on the orifice reducer present in many essential oil jars. Mountain Rose Herbs at www. mountainroseherbs.com is a good source for glass droppers; Wholesale Supplies Plus at www.wholesalesuppliesplus.com is a good source for plastic droppers.

Signature Recipe #1: Rollers

Ingredients:

> 5 ounces olive oil
> 2 ounces sunflower oil
> ½ ounce apricot kernel oil
> 30 drops jojoba

1. Weigh out the olive, sunflower and apricot kernel oils into a pint-sized mason jar with a lid.
2. Add the jojoba and stir to combine.
3. Use a dropper or suction bulb to fill your roller jars. Be sure to leave room for the roller balls to fit inside, plus a little bit more room for essential oils.
4. Proceed to the desired variation and add the essential oils.
5. Place the ball into the roller and secure it firmly. If your rollers came with a tool, use it to press the ball down with less effort.
6. Cap the roller.
7. Invert, return to the upright position and shake sixty seconds.

Dream

Add the following to your roller that contains the signature recipe:

3 drops ylang ylang essential oil

2 drops bergamot essential oil

2 drops tangerine essential oil

2 drops clary sage essential oil

Equinox

Add the following to your roller that contains the signature recipe:

3 drops orange essential oil

3 drops tangerine essential oil

2 drops spearmint essential oil

1 drop tea tree essential oil

Lavender

Add the following to your roller that contains the signature recipe:

8 drops lavender essential oil

1 drop clary sage essential oil

Lemon Ginger

Add the following to your roller that contains the signature recipe:

10 drops ginger essential oil

5 drops lemongrass essential oil

Note: as this roller is often used to help with joints, it is formulated at 5%, a higher dilution than the usual 2-3%.

Lighthouse Lemongrass

Add the following to your roller that contains the signature recipe:

6 drops lemongrass essential oil

3 drops tea tree essential oil

Shaman

This roller can help with bruises. Add the following to your roller that contains the signature recipe:

8 drops arnica CO_2 extract (from Eden Botanicals)

5 drops lavender essential oil

2 drops cypress essential oil

Surf

This roller can help with headaches. Add the following to your roller that contains the signature recipe:

4 drops spearmint essential oil

3 drops peppermint essential oil

2 drops rosemary essential oil

Signature Recipe #2: Energetics Rollers

Ingredients:

5 ounces olive oil

2 ounces sunflower oil

½ ounce argan oil

½ ounce apricot kernel oil

30 drops jojoba

1. Weigh out the olive, sunflower, argan and apricot kernel oils into a pint-sized mason jar with a lid.
2. Add the jojoba and stir to combine.
3. Use a dropper or suction bulb to fill your roller jars. Be sure to leave room for the roller balls to fit inside, plus a little bit more room for essential oils.
4. Proceed to the desired variation and add the essential oils.
5. Place the ball into the roller and secure it firmly. If your rollers came with a tool, use it to press the ball down with less effort.
6. Cap the roller.
7. Invert, return to the upright position and shake sixty seconds.

Neroli Ravensara

Add the following to your roller that contains the signature recipe:

6 drops ravensara essential oil

6 drops neroli essential oil (organic 10% from Eden Botanicals, which means this also contains coconut oil as an ingredient)

Palo Santo

Add the following to your roller that contains the signature recipe:

3 drops palo santo essential oil

3 drops vetiver essential oil

4 drops frankincense essential oil (*Boswellia carteri*)

Patchouli Sandalwood

Add the following to your roller that contains the signature recipe:

5 drops patchouli essential oil

3 drops sandalwood essential oil

1 drop ylang ylang essential oil

1 drop clary sage essential oil

Rose Geranium

Add the following to your roller that contains the signature recipe:

6 drops rose geranium essential oil

3 drops ylang ylang essential oil

2 drops rose otto essential oil (Bulgaria 5% from Eden Botanicals, which means this also contains coconut oil as an ingredient)

White Sage

Add the following to your roller that contains the signature recipe:

    6 drops sage essential oil (*Salvia officinalis*)
    2 drops rosemary essential oil
    2 drops lemon essential oil
    2 drops white sage essential oil (*Salvia apiana*)

Menstrual

Add the following to your roller that contains the signature recipe:

    3 drops pettigrain essential oil
    3 drops bergamot essential oil
    1 drop vetiver essential oil
    3 drops clary sage essential oil
    1 drop ginger essential oil

Chakras

Add the following to your roller that contains the signature recipe:

    3 drops pink lotus absolute (from Eden Botanicals)

3 drops lavender essential oil

3 drops lime essential oil

3 drops sandalwood essential oil

NINE

SCRUBS

WHEN IT COMES TO EXFOLIATION, nothing beats a scrub!

Equipment

For all scrubs, a digital kitchen scale is recommended.

It is helpful to have a long skewer, but you can also stir with a standard household spoon.

I recommend a pint-sized mason jar for the Frankincense Facial Scrub, and a glass measuring cup for the lip scrubs.

When you are using essential oils, it is generally more precise to work with either glass or plastic droppers as opposed to relying on the orifice reducer present in many essential oil jars. Mountain Rose Herbs at www. mountainroseherbs.com is a good source for glass droppers;

Wholesale Supplies Plus at www.wholesalesuppliesplus.com is a good source for plastic droppers.

Signature Recipe #1: Frankincense Facial Scrub

I like to store this in a pint-sized mason jar, preferably one that is amber to protect the essential oils.

If like me you like to use a pea-sized amount of this scrub in the shower, you can also fill a small jar for ease of use. Always take care not to drip water into your scrub, as that could lead to contamination. Apply the scrub in gentle circles, rinse, massage, rinse again, massage again, and you should be good.

This scrub is best enjoyed about one per week. It is also suitable for use on other parts of the body if desired.

Ingredients:

6 ounces Himalayan salt, fine or extra fine grain from Saltworks at seasalt.com

2 ½ ounces sunflower oil

20 drops lavender essential oil

10 drops tea tree essential oil

10 drops ylang ylang essential oil

10 drops frankincense essential oil (*Boswellia carteri*)

10 drops myrrh essential oil

1. Weigh salt into a mixing bowl.
2. Pour sunflower oil over the salt.
3. Add essential oils.

4. Stir thoroughly to combine, at least ninety seconds.

5. Transfer to a glass jar with a lid.

Sand Bar Scrub

This is a popular alternative for those with acne prone skin. Simply replace the essential oils in the frankincense facial scrub with just twelve drops of tea tree essential oils.

Signature Recipe #2: Lavender Lip Scrub

This recipe stores beautifully in a small mason jar.

To use, gently rub a small amount on the lips taking care not to apply too much pressure. Remove the scrub by gently brushing it from the lips into the sink. Apply lip balm if desired.

Ingredients:

5 tablespoons brown sugar

2 tablespoons fractionated coconut oil

1 tablespoon honey

24 drops lavender essential oil

1. Combine all ingredients in your glass measuring cup.

2. Stir thoroughly to combine.

3. Transfer to a glass jar with a lid.

Signature Recipe #3: Peppermint Lip Scrub

This recipe stores beautifully in a small mason jar.

To use, gently rub a small amount on the lips taking care not to apply too much pressure. Remove the scrub by gently brushing it from the lips into the sink. Apply lip balm if desired.

5 tablespoons brown sugar

2 tablespoons fractionated coconut oil

1 tablespoon honey

10 drops peppermint essential oil

1. Combine all ingredients in your glass measuring cup.
2. Stir thoroughly to combine.
3. Transfer to a glass jar with a lid.

TEN

ESSENTIAL OIL DIFFUSER BLENDS

IF YOU LIKE to diffuse essential oils, these recipes totaling approximately eighty-five drops fit in 5ml glass jars with orifice reducers. If you do not want to buy 5ml jars in bulk from SKS (item number 4006-00), you can get smaller quantities of 10ml jars from Mountain Rose Herbs and double the recipes.

I like to diffuse just five drops at a time in a mist diffuser, and practice intermittent diffusing for safety. This means thirty-to-sixty minutes on, then thirty-to-sixty minutes off as recommended by the Tisserand Institute.

For more information on essential oil safety, including how it pertains to children, pets and those with certain medical conditions, you may find this website helpful: www.tisserandinstitute.org.

Be sure to store any diffuser blends you make just as you

would other undiluted essential oils, namely, out of reach of children and pets.

Equipment

When you are using essential oils, it is generally more precise to work with either glass or plastic droppers as opposed to relying on the orifice reducer present in many essential oil jars. Mountain Rose Herbs at www.mountainroseherbs.com is a good source for glass droppers; Wholesale Supplies Plus at www.wholesalesuppliesplus.com is a good source for plastic droppers.

Chai

This one is nice for fall and around the holidays.

50 drops orange essential oil

15 drops ginger essential oil

20 drops clove essential oil

Dream

This one tends to put people in a good mood.

40 drops ylang ylang essential oil

12 drops tangerine essential oil

12 drops clary sage essential oil

21 drops bergamot essential oil

Equinox

This one feels like a breath of spring.

    30 drops orange essential oil

    30 drops tangerine essential oil

    16 drops spearmint essential oil

    8 drops tea tree essential oil

Lavender

This one is super relaxing.

    78 drops lavender essential oil

    7 drops clary sage essential oil

Lemon Ginger

This one is nice in the kitchen.

    75 drops lemongrass essential oil

    15 drops ginger essential oil

Neroli Ravensara

This one is transportive.

    45 drops ravensara essential oil

    40 drops neroli essential oil (organic 10% from Eden Botanicals)

Palo Santo

This is a personal favorite energetically speaking.

26 drops palo santo essential oil

26 drops vetiver essential oil

33 drops frankincense essential oil (*Boswellia carteri*)

Patchouli Sandalwood

A classic combination.

60 drops patchouli essential oil

15 drops sandalwood essential oil

5 drops ylang ylang essential oil

5 drops clary sage essential oil

Surf

This one is great for cutting through the fog.

40 drops spearmint essential oil

30 drops peppermint essential oil

15 drops rosemary essential oil

Rose Geranium

Diffuse this when you need to be gentle with yourself and others.

35 drops rose geranium essential oil

20 drops ylang ylang essential oil

30 drops rose otto essential oil (Bulgaria 5% from Eden Botanicals)

White Sage

Clearing and awesome.

50 drops sage essential oil (*Salvia officinalis*)
15 drops rosemary essential oil
15 drops lemon essential oil
5 drops white sage essential oil (*Salvia apiana*)

PART TWO

ELEVEN

CASTILE SOAP

THE ONLY THREE ingredients you need to make clean castile soap are: extra virgin olive oil, distilled water and sodium hydroxide aka lye. Other ingredients can be added for scent, color and texture or to address more specific skincare needs. If you need to source any soap ingredients, you should be able to find everything you need at Brambleberry: www.brambleberry.com, however, for some of the more exotic essential oils, check out Mountain Rose Herbs at www.mountainroseherbs.com and/or Eden Botanicals at www.edenbotanicals.com.

Extra virgin olive oil is the best soap ingredient in my experience because olive oil is a natural humectant, which means that it does not dry skin the way something like a 100% coconut oil bar might. But not all olive oils are created equal, and some of them are not even really olive oil. If you ever experience an overflowing soap pot, chances are you used a counterfeit or adulterated oil. Based on my experience, look for olive oils that say that they are a product of multiple countries like: Portugal, Greece, Spain, Tunisia etc. For some reason, these *cuvees* tend to be the most reliable.

Sodium hydroxide mixed into distilled water forms the classic lye solution for making bar soap. But there are a few important things to understand about lye before soapmaking. First, the *least chemically intensive route* to true soap means using modern sodium hydroxide. The sodium molecules and the hydroxide molecules interact with the fatty acid chains in the plant fat to cause the processes of hydrolysis and ionization that together create the soapmaking reaction called *saponification*. When saponification is complete, lye is no longer present in the soap. Rather, you now have soap and glycerin. Occasionally you see soap ingredients with the labeling "saponified oils of," which is a way to label bar soap that was made with lye without actually having to say so.

Glycerin Explained

Glycerin shimmers on top of soap at the end of processing and is best stirred right back in and retained—it's great for your skin. By contrast, industrial mass producers typically skim the glycerin off of soap to resell it. One of the uses for glycerin is to create soap *bases*, which are the things you see for the kind of soap called melt and pour. One of the reasons some people like melt and pour is that you don't have to work directly with lye, and, unlike Castile soap made from scratch, melt and pour soap lends itself to being put into novelty shaped molds.

My major issue with melt and pour soap bases is that I have not yet found an acceptable ingredient list after drilling down into the specifics. I will never forget researching an "organic" soap base, which at first pass had a good ingredient list, but also contained a disclaimer about ingredients "incidental" to manufacture not being disclosed. In my former attorney mind, that just defeats the whole purpose. Would you season your organic salad with spices containing undisclosed ingredients? Of course not.

Fear of Lye

The number one reason people give me for not attempting soap at home is fear of lye. Let's break it down so that you have the knowledge you need to get over the fear factor.

Stinging Lye

Some people think of stories from the old days and associate lye with stinging soap. The soap we make with modern sodium hydroxide avoids this problem. All of my recipes are *super-fatted*, which means that there is extra plant fat to ensure that all of the lye transforms into soap and glycerin in such a way as to leave no extra lye. In the olden days, people typically made soap with *potassium hydroxide* (confusingly also called lye) by letting rainwater accumulate over wood ashes until a chicken feather dissolved immediately upon contact in the solution. They had to make educated guesses but never knew precisely the strength of their lye solution, which could lead to an excess of lye resulting in stinging skin. Nowadays, potassium hydroxide is primarily used to achieve saponification for liquid soaps.

Burning Lye

Some people associate lye with burns, and for good reason. Sodium hydroxide solution is so incredible basic as to act like strong acid. So when you make your lye solution, it is recommended to wear appropriate long-sleeved shirts, pants, an apron, eye protection and the kind of rubber gloves that are rated for sodium hydroxide, usually blue. It is also necessary to make a neutralizing solution with warm water, dish soap and white vinegar in which to neutralize all equipment that comes in contact with your lye solution. In the event of a lye burn, rinse immediately with water. Opinions differ on the subject, but a splash of straight vinegar has also worked for me on occasion.

Risky Lye

You must manage the risk associated with working with sodium hydroxide solution. That means working in a controlled, well-ventilated environment with no children or pets in proximity. Ingesting lye solution can be fatal. And the fumes that get kicked off when you mix lye should not be inhaled directly. Personally, I recommend wearing a respirator that filters organic vapors (OV) when mixing lye, then leaving the solution alone in a secure location for five minutes to let the fumes clear out a bit before proceeding.

Plumbing Lye

Some people correctly associate lye with drain opening chemicals, however, the plumbing grade of sodium hydroxide contains gray flecks and should NEVER be used in soapmaking.

Sourcing Lye

Select only grades of lye that are pure white. My personal preference is *food grade* sodium hydroxide from Duda Diesel at www.dudadiesel.com. It sounds weird to call lye food grade, but lye solution is sometimes used by the food industry for things like giving pretzels their distinctive crust.

The food grade Red Hot Devil brand lye from Duda looks like white sugar and can blow around more easily than sodium hydroxide flakes. So for beginners who are nervous about lye, I highly recommend the sodium hydroxide flakes available through Brambleberry at www.brambleberry.com because they won't blow around.

Storing Lye

Your sodium hydroxide must be stored in climate control and away from any potential sources of moisture. If stored in too much humidity, it can pull moisture from the air and crystal-lize, or worse. If ever you open your lye and find that it has crystallized, it is no longer usable for soap making because it has taken on extra water molecules that will completely throw off everything about your super-fatted soap recipe.

Exploding Lye

Commit this sentence to memory: Snow falls on a lake. Every time you make lye solution, you must mix lye into the water, never, ever the reverse. Because if you add water into a cup of lye, you will create a dangerous volcanic reaction.

Snow falls on a lake. Snow falls on a lake. Snow falls on a lake.

I believe in a belt-and-suspenders approach to lye safety. So when we make soap, the sodium hydroxide is always measured into a smaller glass cup size than we use for the distilled water. It makes perfect sense to pour from small into big, ensuring that snow always falls on the lake.

Hot Lye

Understand that when you mix your lye solution, it rapidly increases in temperature. But with the soapmaking technique that I am teaching, it is not necessary to know with precision the temperature of your lye solution, so you do not have to worry about taking its temperature.

Why Lye?

It's gut check time. Having absorbed all of this information about lye, why would anyone want to work with it? Let's go back to where we started: working with modern sodium hydroxide is the least chemically intensive route to make real soap, and, therefore the preferred method for making it clean.

Dedicated Equipment

If you're ready to work with lye, you should commit to using dedicated soapmaking equipment. Fortunately, it's a pretty short list. Every time you make soap you will need:

SAFETY GEAR: apron, gloves, eye protection are the minimum; an OV respirator is optional but recommended

CROCKPOT: standard size, not a tiny one. DO NOT use an Instapot or pressure cooker. You will be using an old school crockpot for soapmaking

STICK BLENDER: also called an immersion blender; make sure to choose one that is either in one piece, or is a two piece that attaches very securely. It would not be safe to be blending raw soap and have your stick blender break apart

· · ·

MEASURING CUPS: You will need a four-cup and a two-cup heat resistant glass measure like Pyrex. They should be new or in good condition to be up to the challenge of lye. It will also be helpful to have a one-cup glass measure for your essential oils

DIGITAL SCALE: This is a must. Please make sure that it can hold at least five pounds.

PLASTIC TRASHCAN or bucket that holds your neutral-izing solution, plus white vinegar and dish soap for the solution

SET OF MIXING BOWLS: 5, 3 and 1.5 quarts are great sizes to use. It is acceptable to use stainless steel bowls because the lye solution will not come into contact with them

SILICONE FLEXIBLE SPATULA (or two)

TWO LONG HANDLED spoons that are made of heavy plastic, not metal, as they will be coming into contact with lye solution and metal can react. At least one of these spoons must not be slotted.

. . .

POT HOLDERS, oven gloves or the equivalent for when you lift the hot crock out of its housing, and a heat proof pad or trivet upon which to place the crock.

IT IS helpful to have a couple of skewers or mixing sticks for working with the essential oils

SPONGE FOR CLEANING your soap dishes.

A SOAP MOLD AND LINER. Ideally, you can make or buy a wooden soap loaf mold in 5-pound dimensions, and purchase a compatible silicone liner. But you can also line just about any solid form with wax paper, including a glass 13 x 9 dish, which would yield soap to cut like you would for brownies.

AND AFTER MAKING SOAP, you may also like to have:

A SOAP CUTTER, which looks like a bench scraper, either straight or crinkled. Molds, liners and soap cutters are available through Brambleberry at brambleberry.com. Soap can also be cut with a kitchen knife, but cutters typically yield a nicer looking bar.

.   .   .

OPTIONAL SOAP PACKAGING. If you want to box your soap, it is important to choose boxes that have a cutout so that the soap can breathe. If using a 5-pound loaf mold, my favorite boxes are the ones with rectangle windows at Wholesale Supplies Plus at www.wholesalesuppliesplus.com. One of my pet peeves is soap that rattles around inside the box. You can add a small ball of parchment paper in the bottom of the box to better anchor your soap.

OPTIONAL SOAP LABELS that list all of the ingredients. If you need large professional quantities, Lightning Labels is amazing: www.lightninglabels.com. But for many years I printed my own labels at home, and found what I needed at a reasonable price from www.onlinelabels.com.

Signature Recipe: Castile Soap

For your neutralizing solution, combine water with one tablespoon of liquid dish soap and 1/4-cup white vinegar and set aside to near where you will be mixing your lye.

Ingredients:

54 ounces extra virgin olive oil

16 ounces distilled water

7 ounces sodium hydroxide aka lye

Gather all of the equipment you need for soapmaking and prepare your workspace.

Plug in the crockpot and set it to preheat using the low setting and with the lid off.

Put on your apron.

Make your neutralizing solution by filling your bucket about two-thirds with warm water, adding dish soap and vinegar. Set it aside near where you plan to mix the lye solution.

WEIGH out your olive oil on the digital scale and set it aside. If your scale shows pounds, 54 ounces is the same as 3 lbs 6 ounces. If you over-pour up to a ½ ounce, that's okay, but please take care not to under-pour or excessively over-pour

WEIGH out your distilled water into your 4-cup glass measuring cup. It must be exactly 16 ounces, which may appear on your scale as 1 lb. Set aside where you plan to mix the lye solution

PUT ON YOUR RESPIRATOR, if using, followed by your eye protection and gloves. Open up the lye and weigh it out into your 2-cup glass measuring cup. It must be exactly 7 ounces. If you over-pour, use a spoon to quickly pull the excess out and back into the lye canister, then slide the spoon into your neutralizing solution. Be sure to close the lye canister, as it should not be sitting out open

SNOW FALLS ON THE LAKE. Slowly stir the lye into the water using your non-slotted, long-handled plastic spoon. It will take about a minute to make sure that all of the lye is dissolved, and the solution will be cloudy at this point.

OPTIONAL STEP: if there is still lye stuck inside the smaller cup after you have emptied it fully into the distilled water, you can very carefully use your mixing spoon to move some of the lye solution back into the smaller cup, swirl it around to collect the stray lye, then pour it into the larger solution. It is important to capture all of the lye, but be very careful and deliberate in your movements if you need to do this.

GENTLY PLACE the lye mixing spoon and the now empty measuring cup into the neutralizing solution. Wash your gloved hands if you can and then carefully remove your gloves and exit the room. Once you have exited, remove the goggles and respirator if using and wait five minutes.

BRING your goggles back into the soap room so that they are still handy. Using your silicone spatula, release all of the extra virgin olive oil into the pre-heated crockpot.

MAKE sure that your stick blender is plugged in and close to the crockpot.

PUT YOUR GOGGLES BACK ON, then your gloves, care-fully carry the lye solution over to the crockpot, pour it in taking care not to splash, and place the now empty cup in the neutralizing solution

WHILE THE STICK blender is still off, use it to stir the pot a few times then, beginning on the lowest setting, start blending and get a feel for it. Take care not to splash. If the blender feels stuck to the bottom of the pot, turn it off then gently tilt it to release any pressure. When you are comfortable, go to the higher setting.

CONTINUE STICK blending until it reaches the consistency of thick pudding, known as *trace*. You can confirm you're at trace by turning off the stick blender, then using it to trace a mark on top of the soap. If the mark holds, you're there.

CAREFULLY TAP the stick blender on the side of the crock to get as much of the raw soap into the pot as possible. Then unplug it and get the dirty part into your neutralizing solution, taking care not to submerge the machinery or plug.

COVER THE CROCKPOT and set a timer for one hour.

STILL WEARING GLOVES, wash everything that went into the neutralizing solution using dish soap and your dedicated sponge. Before washing the stick blender, gently wipe out what you can with paper towels to minimize the amount of raw soap going down the drain. Once all of these items are clean, discard the neutralizing solution and rinse out your bucket.

AT THIS POINT, you can take your gloves off if desired and wash the bowl you used for the olive oil and your silicone spatula. Dry the spatula because you will be using it again when molding the soap.

. . .

CHECK the soap at the one-hour mark. It's best to look through the clear lid, but if you must peek you can just get the lid back on fast.

YOU SHOULD SEE that from the outside in, what was opaque is turning to gel. The soap will be done saponifying when all of the opacity is gone, and a common pattern is called *waves over island*. The gel 'waves' ultimately consume the opaque 'island.' You probably only have minimal gel at this point, so set the timer for another 30 minutes.

OPTIONAL STEP: if you are going to be adding other ingredients like essential oils and exfoliation, just make sure you have what you are planning to use. Don't measure out the essential oils yet, but have the ones you are using near the digital scale along with your stirring utensil and 1-cup glass measure. You can go ahead and measure out any other add-ins at this point in your 1.5-quart mixing bowl.

· · ·

CHECK the soap at the ninety-minute mark. It is likely finished or almost finished. You want to see the uniform gel color, no opacity. If it's not yet finished, replace the cover. Once you're there, turn off the crockpot, use your potholders or oven gloves to remove the pot and place it onto a heat resistant surface or trivet.

THE SOAP WILL BE EXTREMELY hot. Carefully remove the lid, then take a long handled spoon and thoroughly stir your soap to release some of the heat.

OPTIONAL STEP: measure out your essential oils into the 1-cup measure. Mix multiple oils in the cup briefly with a skewer before adding them to the soap. Then add the essential oils to the soap in three additions, stirring the soap with your long-handled spoon to thoroughly combine in between additions.

· · ·

ONCE EVERYTHING IS THOROUGHLY STIRRED, use your long handled spoon together with your silicone spatula to move the soap into your mold. If using a log mold, start filling from one end and work your way to the other. Once all of the soap is in the mold, if you want to tap it down using your hand like a trowel you can, but it will still have some heat. You should hold the mold securely at both ends and tap it on the table a few times, then set it in a place where it will not be disturbed for 24 hours.

YOU DID IT! Now wash your remaining dishes and be sure to soak the soap pot after it is reasonably cooler. The easiest way to clean a soap pot is to just let it soak overnight. The next day:

CAREFULLY REMOVE your soap from the mold and make your desired cuts. If using a 5-lb loaf mold, a nice thickness of bars would be to cut 15 bars, but it is a matter of personal preference.

ONCE YOUR SOAP IS CUT, place the bars on a flat surface lined with parchment or wax paper and stand them up so the air can circulate and they are not touching each other. Technically, if you are in dire need of soap, you could use it, taking care to shake excess water off afterwards and storing it standing up so that air can circulate. But your soap will perform better the longer you age it, and if you can wait a week for your first bar and let the others age for a month or so, you may feel the difference in the hardness, creaminess and lather.

FOR THE FOLLOWING VARIATIONS, the additional ingredients get added after the soap has been thoroughly stirred to release some heat, unless otherwise noted.

Lemon Ginger

This one is nice for achy joints.

$^5/_8$ ounce lemongrass essential oil

¼ ounce lemon essential oil

½ ounce ginger essential oil

Lavender Sea Salt

This one is so relaxing.

1 ounce lavender essential oil

$^1/_8$ ounce sea salt (no more!)

I like the Lavender Sea Salt from www.hatterassaltworks.com. If you are using hand-harvested salt and the salt crystals are large, be sure to crush them down with your fingers a bit before adding to your soap to avoid too large crystals that can cause problems like attracting moisture.

Surf

A bestseller that is so refreshing!

¾ ounce spearmint essential oil

$^1/_8$ ounce peppermint essential oil

$^3/_8$ ounce rosemary essential oil

$^1/_8$ ounce sea salt

¼ ounce ground kelp

I like the Rosemary Sea Salt from www. hatterassaltworks.com. If you are using hand-harvested salt and the salt crystals are large, be sure to crush them down with your fingers a bit before adding to your soap to avoid too large crystals that can cause problems like attracting moisture.

Sometimes in the winter, I would vary the essential oils in the Surf soap to bring out the peppermint as follows:

¾ ounce peppermint essential oil

$^3/_8$ ounce rosemary essential oil

¼ ounce spearmint essential oil

Equinox

Equinox is a great travel bar.

¾ ounce orange essential oil

¾ ounce tangerine essential oil

½ ounce spearmint essential oil

¼ ounce tea tree essential oil

Chai

A seasonal favorite.

1 ounce orange essential oil

$^3/_8$ ounce clove essential oil

$^1/_8$ ounce ginger essential oil

1 $^3/_8$ ounces ground coffee if strong exfoliation is desired

This soap is also nice when fennel essential oil is substituted for ginger essential oil.

Dream

Dream is dreamy!

$^5/_8$ ounce tangerine essential oil

$^5/_8$ ounce ylang ylang essential oil

$^3/_8$ ounce bergamot essential oil

$^3/_8$ ounce orange essential oil

1 tablespoon orange peel powder if some exfoliation is desired.

Patchulio

Patchouli plus orange is delightful.

1 ounce lavender essential oil

$^3/_8$ ounce rosemary essential oil

$^3/_8$ ounce patchouli essential oil

$^3/_8$ ounce orange essential oil

Palo Santo

Palo Santo is great for positivity.

$\frac{1}{4}$ ounce palo santo essential oil

$\frac{1}{8}$ ounce vetiver essential oil

$\frac{5}{8}$ ounce frankincense essential oil

Patchouli Sandalwood

Patchouli Sandalwood is a classic combination.

1 ounce patchouli essential oil

$\frac{1}{8}$ ounce sandalwood essential oil

$\frac{1}{8}$ ounce ylang ylang essential oil

$\frac{1}{8}$ ounce clary sage essential oil

White Sage

Clearing; a personal favorite after absorbing crowd energy.

$\frac{5}{8}$ ounce sage essential oil (*Salvia officinalis*)

$\frac{1}{2}$ ounce rosemary essential oil

$\frac{1}{2}$ ounce lemon essential oil

$\frac{1}{8}$ ounce white sage essential oil (*Salvia apiana*)

2 tablespoons finely ground white sage leaves if exfoliation is desired. You can grind your own in a spice grinder, or even a countertop blender.

Rose Geranium

Rose Geranium feels like love.

$^5/_8$ ounce rose geranium essential oil

½ ounce ylang ylang essential oil

$^1/_8$ ounce rose otto essential oil (Bulgaria 5% from Eden Botanicals, which means this also contains coconut oil as an ingredient)

Neroli Ravensara

Neroli Ravensara is a sophisticated bar.

1 ounce ravensara essential oil

¼ ounce neroli essential oil (organic 10% from Eden Botanicals, which means this also contains coconut oil as an ingredient)

Citrus Mint

Citrus Mint is bright and refreshing.

5/8 grapefruit essential oil

3/8 lime essential oil

3/8 lemon essential oil

3/8 spearmint essential oil

Baby Soap

¼ ounce lavender essential oil

For babies, the best soap is either unscented, or made

with just a hint of lavender. Care must be taken to ensure that no soap comes into contact with the eyes because it will sting. The ingredients used to make items tear-free just do not fall into the *clean* category.

Argan Rose

I designed as a holistic skincare bar. You will need two ounces of argan oil to substitute for two ounces of extra virgin olive oil at the beginning of the soapmaking process (use 52 ounces extra virgin olive oil and 2 ounces argan oil).

You will also need to add in 1 TB activated charcoal and 1 TB white pumice shortly after you begin stick blending and before trace.

¼ ounce lime essential oil

¼ ounce lavender essential oil

¼ ounce tea tree essential oil

¼ ounce rose otto essential oil that has been diluted into a 10% concentration in fractionated coconut oil if cost is a factor. Note that if you use diluted essential oil and are labeling ingredients, it is necessary to include the coconut oil in your ingredient list.

Sandalwood Lime

This bar is expensive to produce, but worth it!

¾ ounce lime essential oil

1/8 ounce sandalwood essential oil

1/8 ounce organic vanilla CO_2 extract diluted to 10%

from Eden Botanicals (include the coconut oil in your ingredient list)

½ ounce lavender

Sandalwood

My first recipe with sandalwood essential oil in soap.

1/8 ounce sandalwood essential oil

½ ounce ylang ylang essential oil

½ ounce clary sage essential oil

Juniper Berry

I liked this combination with olive leaf powder.

¾ ounce grapefruit essential oil

3/8 ounce rosemary essential oil

1/8 ounce juniper essential oil

1 teaspoon olive leaf powder added with the essential oils at the end of the soapmaking process

Longboard

Exotic and woodsy.

1 ½ ounce cedarwood essential oil

1/8 ounce clary sage essential oil

1/8 ounce patchouli essential oil

1 teaspoon ground kelp, added along with the essential oils at the end of the soapmaking process.

Lavender Lemongrass

Lavender and Lemongrass is a great combo!

   1 ¼-ounce lavender essential oil

   ¼ ounce lemongrass essential oil

   1/8 ounce grapefruit essential oil

   Optional: 1-ounce dried lavender buds to be mixed in at the end of soapmaking with the essential oils

TWELVE

LIGHTHOUSE LEMONGRASS SOAP

THIS IS the recipe for one of my bestselling soaps of all time. A farmer's market favorite with a strong lemongrass scent profile, I designed this soap to get a head start on the mosquitoes. By dissolving the lye in a coffee solution, this soap has deodorizing properties that are particularly excellent, but it does not end up smelling like coffee. This soap was part of my *bug magnet special*, together with Lighthouse Lemongrass Spray and the Shaman Super Stick.

Signature Recipe: Lighthouse Lemongrass Soap

For your neutralizing solution, combine water with one tablespoon of liquid dish soap and 1/4-cup white vinegar and set aside to near where you will be mixing your lye.

Ingredients:

54 ounces extra virgin olive oil

16 ounces strong coffee brewed with distilled water

7 ounces sodium hydroxide aka lye

1 ounce lemongrass essential oil

½ ounce tea tree essential oil

First brew strong coffee using distilled water, then let it cool down to room temperature.

Gather all of the equipment you need for soapmaking and prepare your workspace.

Plug in the crockpot and set it to preheat using the low setting and with the lid off.

Put on your apron.

Make your neutralizing solution by filling your bucket about two-thirds with warm water, adding dish soap and vinegar. Set it aside near where you plan to mix the lye solution.

WEIGH out your olive oil on the digital scale and set it aside. If your scale shows pounds, 54 ounces is the same as 3 lbs 6 ounce. If you over-pour up to a ½ ounce, that's ok, but please take care not to under-pour or excessively over-pour

WEIGH out your coffee into your 4-cup glass measuring cup. It must be exactly 16 ounces, which may appear on your scale as 1 lb and set aside where you plan to mix the lye solution

PUT ON YOUR RESPIRATOR, if using, followed by your eye protection and gloves. Open up the lye and weigh it out into your 2-cup glass measuring cup. It must be exactly 7 ounces. If you over-pour, use a spoon to quickly pull the excess out and back into the lye canister, then slide the spoon into your neutralizing solution. Be sure to close the lye canister, as it should not be sitting out open

SNOW FALLS ON THE LAKE. Slowly stir the lye into the coffee using your non-slotted, long-handled plastic spoon. It will take about a minute to make sure that all of the lye is dissolved, and the solution will be cloudy at this point.

OPTIONAL STEP: if there is still lye stuck inside the smaller cup after you have emptied it fully into the coffee, you can very carefully use your mixing spoon to move some of the lye solution back into the smaller cup, swirl it around to collect the stray lye, then pour it into the larger solution. It is important to capture all of the lye, but be very careful and deliberate in your movements if you need to do this.

GENTLY PLACE the lye mixing spoon and the now empty measuring cup into the neutralizing solution. Wash your gloved hands if you can and then carefully remove your gloves and exit the room. Once you have exited, remove the goggles and respirator if using and wait five minutes.

. . .

BRING your goggles back into the soap room so that they are still handy. Using your silicone spatula, release all of the extra virgin olive oil into the pre-heated crockpot.

MAKE sure that your stick blender is plugged in and close to the crockpot.

PUT YOUR GOGGLES BACK ON, then your gloves, carefully carry the lye solution over to the crockpot, pour it in taking care not to splash, and place the now empty cup in the neutralizing solution

WHILE THE STICK blender is still off, use it to stir the pot a few times then, beginning on the lowest setting, start blending and get a feel for it. Take care not to splash. If the blender feels stuck to the bottom of the pot, turn it off then gently tilt it to release any pressure. When you are comfortable, go to the higher setting. Continue stick blending until it reaches the consistency of thick pudding, known as *trace*. You can confirm you're at trace by turning off the stick blender, then using it to trace a mark on top of the soap. If the mark holds, you're there.

CAREFULLY TAP the stick blender on the side of the crock to get as much of the raw soap into the pot as possible. Then unplug it and get the dirty part into your neutralizing solution, taking care not to submerge the machinery or plug.

COVER THE CROCKPOT and set a timer for one hour.

STILL WEARING GLOVES, wash everything that went into the neutralizing solution using dish soap and your dedicated sponge. Before washing the stick blender, gently wipe out what you can with paper towels to minimize the amount of raw soap going down the drain. Once all of these items are clean, discard the neutralizing solution and rinse out your bucket.

AT THIS POINT, you can take your gloves off if desired and wash the bowl you used for the olive oil and your silicone spatula. Dry the spatula because you will be using it again when molding the soap.

CHECK the soap at the one-hour mark. It's best to look through the clear lid, but if you must peek you can just get the lid back on fast. You should see that from the outside in, what was opaque is turning to gel. The soap will be done saponifying when all of the opacity is gone. You will probably only have minimal gel at this point, so set the timer for another 30 minutes.

. . .

LOCATE your lemongrass and tea tree essential oils, but don't measure them out yet. Place them near the digital scale along with your stirring utensil and 1-cup glass measure.

CHECK the soap at the ninety-minute mark. It is likely finished or almost finished. You want to see the uniform gel color, no opacity. If it's not yet finished, replace the cover. Once you're there, turn off the crockpot, use your potholders or oven gloves to remove the pot and place it onto a heat resistant surface or trivet.

THE SOAP WILL BE EXTREMELY hot. Carefully remove the lid, then take a long handled spoon and thoroughly stir your soap to release some of the heat.

MEASURE out your lemongrass and tea tree essential oils in the 1-cup measure, then mix them briefly with a skewer before adding them to the soap in three additions, stirring the soap with your long-handled spoon to thoroughly combine in between additions.

ONCE EVERYTHING IS THOROUGHLY STIRRED, use your long handled spoon together with your silicone spatula to move the soap into your mold. If using a log mold, start filling from one end and work your way to the other. Once all of the soap is in the mold, if you want to tap it down using your hand like a trowel you can, but it will still have some heat. You should hold the mold securely at both ends and tap it on the table a few times, then set it in a place where it will not be disturbed for 24 hours.

YOU DID IT! Now wash your remaining dishes and be sure to soak the soap pot after it is reasonably cooler. The easiest way to clean a soap pot is to just let it soak overnight. The next day:

CAREFULLY REMOVE your soap from the mold and make your desired cuts. If using a 5-lb loaf mold, a nice thickness of bars would be to cut 15 bars, but it is a matter of personal preference.

ONCE YOUR SOAP IS CUT, place the bars on a flat surface lined with parchment or wax paper and stand them up so the air can circulate and they are not touching each other.

TECHNICALLY, if you are in dire need of soap, you could use it, taking care to shake excess water off afterwards and storing it standing up so that air can circulate. But your soap will perform better the longer you age it, and if you can wait a week for your first bar and let the others age for a month or so, you may feel the difference in the hardness, creaminess and lather.

THIRTEEN

SHEA BUTTER SOAP

IN A WAY, the first two Signature soap recipes are kind of like playing defense—made with one hundred percent extra virgin olive oil, they are gentle and universal. But now it's time for offense. Shea butter soap is where we turn for deep skin nourishment. The Shaman version was beloved by those with eczema as a head-to-toe bar, yet also extremely popular among those with mature skin as a facial bar. The Char version was my bestselling skincare bar, particularly for those who are acne-prone and for those wish to use a charcoal soap that is not too harsh.

To make Shea Butter soap, you will need access to a stovetop or a hot plate and a large saucepan or dutch oven.

Signature Recipe: Shea Butter Soap

Ingredients:

    24 ounces extra virgin olive oil

    8 ounces avocado oil

    2 ounces castor oil

    2 ounces grapeseed oil

    12 ounces coconut oil (melts at 76 degrees)

    8 ounces shea butter (melts at 90 degrees)

    16 ounces distilled water

    $7\,^5/_8$ ounces sodium hydroxide aka lye

    Neutralizing Solution Ingredients:

    Water

    TB dish soap

    ¼ cup white vinegar

Gather all of the equipment you need for soapmaking and prepare your workspace.

Plug in the crockpot and set it to preheat using the low setting and with the lid off.

Put on your apron.

Make your neutralizing solution by filling your bucket about 2/3 with warm water, adding dish soap and vinegar. Set it aside near where you plan to mix the lye solution

WEIGH out your liquid oils of olive, avocado, castor and grapeseed on the digital scale, it is ok to combine them in the same bowl and then set it aside. If your scale shows pounds, 24 ounces is the same as 1 lbs 8 ounce for the olive oil. If you over-pour up to a ½ ounce, that's ok, but please take care not to under-pour or excessively over-pour

WEIGH out your coconut oil and shea butter into your 5-7 quart pot or dutch oven. If it weighs too much for your digital scale, measure the ingredients using a bowl, then transfer them to the pot and set aside.

WEIGH out your distilled water into your 4-cup glass measuring cup. It must be exactly 16 ounces, which may appear on your scale as 1 lb and set aside where you plan to mix the lye solution

PUT ON YOUR RESPIRATOR, if using, followed by your eye protection and gloves. Open up the lye and weigh it out into your 2-cup glass measuring cup. It must be exactly $7\,^5/_8$ ounces. If you over-pour, use a spoon to quickly pull the excess out and back into the lye canister, then slide the spoon into your neutralizing solution. Be sure to close the lye canister, as it should not be sitting out open

SNOW FALLS ON THE LAKE. Slowly stir the lye into the water using your non-slotted, long-handled plastic spoon. It will take about a minute to make sure that all of the lye is dissolved, and the solution will be cloudy at this point.

. . .

OPTIONAL STEP: if there is still lye stuck inside the smaller cup after you have emptied it fully into the distilled water, you can very carefully use your mixing spoon to move some of the lye solution back into the smaller cup, swirl it around to collect the stray lye, then pour it into the larger solution. It is important to capture all of the lye, but be very careful and deliberate in your movements if you need to do this.

GENTLY PLACE the lye mixing spoon and the now empty measuring cup into the neutralizing solution. Wash your gloved hands if you can and then carefully remove your gloves and exit the room. Once you have exited, remove the goggles and respirator if using and wait five minutes.

IF YOU ARE MELTING the coconut oil and shea butter in another room, take this time to do so over medium high heat. Be careful—the oils get hot and you don't want to splash.

REMEMBER to bring your goggles back into the soap room so that they are still handy. If you have not already melted the coconut oil and shea butter, do so now, using medium high heat.

. . .

USING YOUR SILICONE SPATULA, release the coconut oil and shea butter, followed by the liquid oils of olive, avocado, castor and grapeseed into the pre-heated crockpot.

MAKE sure that your stick blender is plugged in and close to the crockpot.

PUT YOUR GOGGLES BACK ON, then your gloves, carefully carry the lye solution over to the crockpot, pour it in taking care not to splash, and place the now empty cup in the neutralizing solution

WHILE THE STICK blender is still off, use it to stir the pot a few times then, beginning on the lowest setting, start blending and get a feel for it. Take care not to splash. If the blender feels stuck to the bottom of the pot, turn it off then gently tilt it to release any pressure. When you are comfortable, go to the higher setting. Continue stick blending until it reaches the consistency of thick pudding, known as *trace*. You can confirm you're at trace by turning off the stick blender, then using it to trace a mark on top of the soap. If the mark holds, you're there. This Signature soap recipe comes to trace faster than the others.

. . .

CAREFULLY TAP the stick blender on the side of the crock to get as much of the raw soap into the pot as possible. Then unplug it and get the dirty part into your neutralizing solution, taking care not to submerge the machinery or plug.

COVER THE CROCKPOT and set a timer for thirty minutes.

STILL WEARING GLOVES, wash everything that went into the neutralizing solution using dish soap and your dedicated sponge. Before washing the stick blender, gently wipe out what you can with paper towels to minimize the amount of raw soap going down the drain. Once all of these items are clean, discard the neutralizing solution and rinse out your bucket.

AT THIS POINT, you can take your gloves off if desired and wash the other dishes and your silicone spatula. Dry the spatula because you will be using it again when molding the soap.

CHECK the soap at the thirty-minute mark. It's best to look through the clear lid, but if you must peek you can just get the lid back on fast. You should see that from the outside in, what was opaque is turning to gel. The soap will be done saponifying when all of the opacity is gone. You probably have about two-thirds gel at this point, so set the timer for another fifteen minutes.

OPTIONAL STEP: if you are going to be adding essential oils, just make sure you have what you are planning to use. Don't measure out the essential oils yet, but have the ones you are using near the digital scale along with your stirring utensil and 1-cup glass measure.

CHECK the soap at the forty-five-minute mark. It is likely finished or almost finished. You want to see the uniform gel color, no opacity. If it's not yet finished, replace the cover. Once you're there, turn off the crockpot, use your potholders or oven gloves to remove the pot and place it onto a heat resistant surface or trivet.

THE SOAP WILL BE EXTREMELY hot. Carefully remove the lid, then take a long handled spoon and thoroughly stir your soap to release some of the heat.

OPTIONAL STEP: measure out your essential oil(s) into the 1-cup measure. Mix multiple oils in the cup briefly with a skewer before adding them to the soap. Then add the essential oils to the soap in three additions, stirring the soap with your long-handled spoon to thoroughly combine in between additions.

ONCE EVERYTHING IS THOROUGHLY STIRRED, use your long handled spoon together with your silicone spatula to move the soap into your mold. If using a log mold, start filling from one end and work your way to the other. Once all of the soap is in the mold, if you want to tap it down using your hand like a trowel you can, but it will still have some heat. You should hold the mold securely at both ends and tap it on the table a few times, then set it in a place where it will not be disturbed for 24 hours.

YOU DID IT! Now wash your remaining dishes and be sure to soak the soap pot after it is reasonably cooler. The easiest way to clean a soap pot is to just let it soak overnight. The next day:

CAREFULLY REMOVE your soap from the mold and make your desired cuts. If using a five pound loaf mold, a nice thickness of bars would be to cut fifteen bars, but it is a matter of personal preference.

ONCE YOUR SOAP IS CUT, place the bars on a flat surface lined with parchment or wax paper and stand them up so the air can circulate and they are not touching each other. Technically, if you are in dire need of soap, you could use it, taking care to shake excess water off afterwards and storing it standing up so that air can circulate. But your soap will perform better the longer you age it, and if you can wait a week for your first bar and let the others age for a month or so, you may feel the difference in the hardness, creaminess and lather.

Shaman

Ingredients:

1 ounce lavender essential oil

$^{3}/_{8}$ ounce tea tree essential oil

Char

2 tablespoons activated charcoal mixed with 2 tablespoons white pumice, to be added very soon after you begin stick blending and before trace. Remember, this soap achieves trace fast. And activated charcoal can make a mess, so work carefully when handling.

$^{3}/_{8}$ ounce tea tree essential oil

FOURTEEN

COCOA BUTTER SOAP

THIS SOAP IS excellent for those who know and love cocoa butter. In the summertime, a smooth cocoa butter bar feels great on crispy skin. In the wintertime, the Sugar Plum variation is a decadent indulgence.

To make Cocoa Butter soap, you will need access to a stovetop or a hot plate and a large saucepan or dutch oven.

Signature Recipe: Cocoa Butter Soap

Ingredients:

24 ounces extra virgin olive oil

12 ounces grapeseed oil

2 ounces castor oil

12 ounces coconut oil (76 degree melt point)

4 ounces cocoa butter, preferably organic in cubes or wafers (90 degree melt point)

16 ounces distilled water

7 $^3/_8$ ounces sodium hydroxide aka lye

Neutralizing Solution Ingredients:

Water

TB dish soap

¼ cup white vinegar

Gather all of the equipment you need for soapmaking and prepare your workspace.

Plug in the crockpot and set it to preheat using the low setting and with the lid off.

Put on your apron.

Make your neutralizing solution by filling your bucket about two-thirds with warm water, adding dish soap and vinegar. Set it aside near where you plan to mix the lye solution.

WEIGH out your liquid oils of olive, grapeseed and castor on the digital scale, it is ok to combine them in the same bowl and then set it aside. If your scale shows pounds, 24 ounces is the same as 1 lbs 8 ounce for the olive oil. If you over-pour up to a ½ ounce, that's ok, but please take care not to under-pour or excessively over-pour

WEIGH out your coconut oil and cocoa butter into your sauce pan or dutch oven. If it weighs too much for your digital scale, measure the ingredients using a bowl, then transfer them to the pot and set aside.

. . .

WEIGH out your distilled water into your 4-cup glass measuring cup. It must be exactly 16 ounces, which may appear on your scale as 1 lb and set aside where you plan to mix the lye solution

PUT ON YOUR RESPIRATOR, if using, followed by your eye protection and gloves. Open up the lye and weigh it out into your 2-cup glass measuring cup. It must be exactly $7\,^3/_8$ ounces. If you over-pour, use a spoon to quickly pull the excess out and back into the lye canister, then slide the spoon into your neutralizing solution. Be sure to close the lye canister, as it should not be sitting out open

SNOW FALLS ON THE LAKE. Slowly stir the lye into the water using your non-slotted, long-handled plastic spoon. It will take about a minute to make sure that all of the lye is dissolved, and the solution will be cloudy at this point.

OPTIONAL STEP: if there is still lye stuck inside the smaller cup after you have emptied it fully into the distilled water, you can very carefully use your mixing spoon to move some of the lye solution back into the smaller cup, swirl it around to collect the stray lye, then pour it into the larger solution. It is important to capture all of the lye, but be very deliberate in your movements if you need to do this.

·   ·   ·

GENTLY PLACE the lye mixing spoon and the now empty measuring cup into the neutralizing solution. Wash your gloved hands if you can and then carefully remove your gloves and exit the room. Once you have exited, remove the goggles and respirator if using and wait five minutes.

IF YOU ARE MELTING the coconut oil and cocoa butter in another room, take this time to do so over medium high heat. Be careful—the oils get hot and you don't want to splash.

REMEMBER to bring your goggles back into the soap room so that they are still handy. If you have not already melted the coconut oil and cocoa butter, do so now, using medium high heat.

USING YOUR SILICONE SPATULA, release the coconut oil and cocoa butter, followed by the liquid oils of olive, castor and grapeseed into the pre-heated crockpot.

MAKE sure that your stick blender is plugged in and close to the crockpot.

PUT YOUR GOGGLES BACK ON, then your gloves, carefully carry the lye solution over to the crockpot, pour it in taking care not to splash, and place the now empty cup in the neutralizing solution.

WHILE THE STICK blender is still off, use it to stir the pot a few times then, beginning on the lowest setting, start blending and get a feel for it. Take care not to splash. If the blender feels stuck to the bottom of the pot, turn it off then gently tilt it to release any pressure. When you are comfortable, go to the higher setting. Continue stick blending until it reaches the consistency of thick pudding, known as *trace*. You can confirm you're at trace by turning off the stick blender, then using it to trace a mark on top of the soap. If the mark holds, you're there. This Signature soap recipe comes to trace faster than the others.

CAREFULLY TAP the stick blender on the side of the crock to get as much of the raw soap into the pot as possible. Then unplug it and get the dirty part into your neutralizing solution, taking care not to submerge the machinery or plug.

COVER THE CROCKPOT and set a timer for forty-five minutes.

STILL WEARING GLOVES, wash everything that went into the neutralizing solution using dish soap and your dedicated sponge. Before washing the stick blender, gently wipe out what you can with paper towels to minimize the amount of raw soap going down the drain. Once all of these items are clean, discard the neutralizing solution and rinse out your bucket.

AT THIS POINT, you can take your gloves off if desired and wash the other dishes and your silicone spatula. Dry the spatula because you will be using it again when molding the soap.

CHECK the soap at the forty-five-minute mark. It's best to look through the clear lid, but if you must peek you can just get the lid back on fast. You should see that from the outside in, what was opaque is turning to gel. The soap will be done saponifying when all of the opacity is gone, and a common pattern is called *waves over island*. The gel waves ultimately consume the opaque island. You probably have about ¾ gel at this point, so set the timer for another 15 minutes.

OPTIONAL STEP: if you are going to be adding essential oils, just make sure you have what you are planning to use. Don't measure out the essential oils yet, but have the ones you are using near the digital scale along with your stirring utensil and 1-cup glass measure.

·　·　·

CHECK the soap at the hour mark. It is likely finished or almost finished. You want to see the uniform gel color, no opacity. Once you're there, turn off the crockpot, use your potholders or oven gloves to remove the pot and place it onto a heat resistant surface or trivet.

THE SOAP WILL BE EXTREMELY hot. Carefully remove the lid, then take a long handled spoon and thoroughly stir your soap to release some of the heat.

OPTIONAL STEP: measure out your essential oils into the 1-cup measure. Mix multiple oils in the cup briefly with a skewer before adding them to the soap. Then add the essential oils to the soap in three additions, stirring the soap with your long-handled spoon to thoroughly combine in between additions.

ONCE EVERYTHING IS THOROUGHLY STIRRED, use your long handled spoon together with your silicone spatula to move the soap into your mold. If using a log mold, start filling from one end and work your way to the other. Once all of the soap is in the mold, if you want to tap it down using your hand like a trowel you can, but it will still have some heat. You should hold the mold securely at both ends and tap it on the table a few times, then set it in a place where it will not be disturbed for 24 hours.

. . .

YOU DID IT! Now wash your remaining dishes and be sure to soak the soap pot after it is reasonably cooler. The easiest way to clean a soap pot is to just let it soak overnight. The next day:

CAREFULLY REMOVE your soap from the mold and make your desired cuts. If using a five pound loaf mold, a nice thickness of bars would be to cut fifteen bars, but it is a matter of personal preference.

ONCE YOUR SOAP IS CUT, place the bars on a flat surface lined with parchment or wax paper and stand them up so the air can circulate and they are not touching each other. Technically, if you are in dire need of soap, you could use it, taking care to shake excess water off afterwards and storing it standing up so that air can circulate. But your soap will perform better the longer you age it, and if you can wait a week for your first bar and let the others age for a month or so, you may feel the difference in the hardness, creaminess and lather.

Bergamot Butterfly

Substitute 16 ounces strong coffee brewed with distilled water

½ ounce grapefruit essential oil

½ ounce bergamot essential oil

½ ounce lavender essential oil

$^1/_8$ ounce patchouli essential oil

Sugar Plum

This was a holiday season favorite.

$^7/_8$ ounce orange essential oil

$^1/_8$ ounce clary sage essential oil

½ ounce bergamot

1 ½ ounces fine brown sugar. You can simply mix it in with the essential oils at the end of the soapmaking process. Alternatively, if you'd like a pretty stripe running up the center of the soap bars, fill the bottom of the mold with half the soap, press it down, sprinkle the sugar on top, then carefully place the rest of the soap on top of the sugar and fill the mold.

FIFTEEN

SHEA AND COCOA BUTTER SOAP

THIS IS the Signature recipe for a soap that has had several names and multiple iterations over the years. When I was first making this soap, I did a tea tree and pumice version called Sand Bar, which later became Tea Tree with some additional essential oils. I also did a calendula and cornmeal version originally called Hula, then much later, Sand Bar. So the following recipes will tie to the original versions of the soap, and if you are looking to make the oft-requested super-exfoliating soap with calendula petals and cornmeal that is awesome for removing sand after the beach, you'll want to make Hula.

To make Shea & Cocoa soap, you will need access to a stovetop or a hot plate and a large saucepan or dutch oven.

Signature Recipe #5: Shea & Cocoa Soap

Ingredients:

　　24 ounces extra virgin olive oil

　　8 ounces sunflower oil

　　2 ounces castor oil

　　4 ounces cocoa butter

　　4 ounces shea butter

　　20 ounces distilled water

　　7 $^3/_8$ ounces sodium hydroxide aka lye

　　Neutralizing Solution Ingredients:

　　Water

　　TB dish soap

　　¼ cup white vinegar

Gather all of the equipment you need for soapmaking and prepare your workspace.

Plug in the crockpot and set it to preheat using the low setting and with the lid off.

Put on your apron.

Make your neutralizing solution by filling your bucket about two-thirds with warm water, adding dish soap and vinegar. Set it aside near where you plan to mix the lye solution.

WEIGH out your liquid oils of olive, sunflower and castor on the digital scale, it is ok to combine them in the same bowl and then set it aside. If your scale shows pounds, 24 ounces is the same as 1 lbs 8 ounces for the olive oil. If you over-pour up to a ½ ounce, that's ok, but please take care not to under-pour or excessively over-pour.

WEIGH OUT YOUR COCONUT OIL, shea and cocoa butter into your sauce pan or dutch oven. If it weighs too much for your digital scale, measure the ingredients using a bowl, then transfer them to the pot and set aside.

WEIGH out your distilled water into your 4-cup glass measuring cup. It must be exactly 20 ounces, which may appear on your scale as 1 lb 4 ounces and set aside where you plan to mix the lye solution.

PUT ON YOUR RESPIRATOR, if using, followed by your eye protection and gloves. Open up the lye and weigh it out into your 2-cup glass measuring cup. It must be exactly $7\,^3/_8$ ounces. If you over-pour, use a spoon to quickly pull the excess out and back into the lye canister, then slide the spoon into your neutralizing solution. Be sure to close the lye canister, as it should not be sitting out open.

SNOW FALLS ON THE LAKE. Slowly stir the lye into the water using your non-slotted, long-handled plastic spoon. It will take about a minute to make sure that all of the lye is dissolved, and the solution will be cloudy at this point.

. . .

OPTIONAL STEP: if there is still lye stuck inside the smaller cup after you have emptied it fully into the distilled water, you can very carefully use your mixing spoon to move some of the lye solution back into the smaller cup, swirl it around to collect the stray lye, then pour it into the larger solution. It is important to capture all of the lye, but be very deliberate in your movements if you need to do this.

GENTLY PLACE the lye mixing spoon and the now empty measuring cup into the neutralizing solution. Wash your gloved hands if you can and then carefully remove your gloves and exit the room. Once you have exited, remove the goggles and respirator if using and wait five minutes.

IF YOU ARE MELTING the coconut oil, shea and cocoa butter in another room, take this time to do so over medium high heat. Be careful—the oils get hot and you don't want to splash.

REMEMBER to bring your goggles back into the soap room so that they are still handy. If you have not already melted the coconut oil, shea and cocoa butter, do so now, using medium high heat.

. . .

USING YOUR SILICONE SPATULA, release the coconut oil, shea and cocoa butter, followed by the liquid oils of olive, castor and sunflower into the pre-heated crockpot.

MAKE sure that your stick blender is plugged in and close to the crockpot.

PUT YOUR GOGGLES BACK ON, then your gloves, carefully carry the lye solution over to the crockpot, pour it in taking care not to splash, and place the now empty cup in the neutralizing solution.

WHILE THE STICK blender is still off, use it to stir the pot a few times then, beginning on the lowest setting, start blending and get a feel for it. Take care not to splash. If the blender feels stuck to the bottom of the pot, turn it off then gently tilt it to release any pressure. When you are comfortable, go to the higher setting. Continue stick blending until it reaches the consistency of thick pudding, known as *trace*. You can confirm you're at trace by turning off the stick blender, then using it to trace a mark on top of the soap. If the mark holds, you're there. This Signature soap recipe comes to trace faster than the others.

· · ·

CAREFULLY TAP the stick blender on the side of the crock to get as much of the raw soap into the pot as possible. Then unplug it and get the dirty part into your neutralizing solution, taking care not to submerge the machinery or plug.

COVER THE CROCKPOT and set a timer for forty-five minutes.

STILL WEARING GLOVES, wash everything that went into the neutralizing solution using dish soap and your dedicated sponge. Before washing the stick blender, gently wipe out what you can with paper towels to minimize the amount of raw soap going down the drain. Once all of these items are clean, discard the neutralizing solution and rinse out your bucket.

AT THIS POINT, you can take your gloves off if desired and wash the other dishes and your silicone spatula. Dry the spatula because you will be using it again when molding the soap.

CHECK the soap at the forty-five-minute mark. It's best to look through the clear lid, but if you must peek you can just get the lid back on fast. You should see that from the outside in, what was opaque is turning to gel. The soap will be done saponifying when all of the opacity is gone, and a common pattern is called *waves over island*. The gel waves ultimately consume the opaque island. You probably have about ¾ gel at this point, so set the timer for another fifteen minutes.

OPTIONAL STEP: if you are going to be adding essential oils, just make sure you have what you are planning to use. Don't measure out the essential oils yet, but have the ones you are using near the digital scale along with your stirring utensil and 1-cup glass measure. If you are adding pumice for Sand Bar/Tea Tree, or calendula, cornmeal and turmeric for Hula, measure that out now.

CHECK the soap at the hour mark. It is likely finished or almost finished. You want to see the uniform gel color, no opacity. Once you're there, turn off the crockpot, use your potholders or oven gloves to remove the pot and place it onto a heat resistant surface or trivet.

THE SOAP WILL BE EXTREMELY hot. Carefully remove the lid, then take a long handled spoon and thoroughly stir your soap to release some of the heat.

OPTIONAL STEP: if using, add pumice or calendula, corn-meal and turmeric now.

. . .

OPTIONAL STEP: measure out your essential oils into the 1-cup measure. Mix multiple oils in the cup briefly with a skewer before adding them to the soap. Then add the essential oils to the soap in three additions, stirring the soap with your long-handled spoon to thoroughly combine in between additions.

ONCE EVERYTHING IS THOROUGHLY STIRRED, use your long handled spoon together with your silicone spatula to move the soap into your mold. If using a log mold, start filling from one end and work your way to the other. Once all of the soap is in the mold, if you want to tap it down using your hand like a trowel you can, but it will still have some heat. You should hold the mold securely at both ends and tap it on the table a few times, then set it in a place where it will not be disturbed for 24 hours.

YOU DID IT! Now wash your remaining dishes and be sure to soak the soap pot after it is reasonably cooler. The easiest way to clean a soap pot is to just let it soak overnight. The next day:

CAREFULLY REMOVE your soap from the mold and make your desired cuts. If using a five-pound loaf mold, a nice thickness of bars would be to cut fifteen bars, but it is a matter of personal preference.

ONCE YOUR SOAP IS CUT, place the bars on a flat surface lined with parchment or wax paper and stand them up so the air can circulate and they are not touching each other. Technically, if you are in dire need of soap, you could use it, taking care to shake excess water off afterwards and storing it standing up so that air can circulate. But your soap will perform better the longer you age it, and if you can wait a week for your first bar and let the others age for a month or so, you may feel the difference in the hardness, creaminess and lather.

Sand Bar

This contains white pumice, which gently exfoliates

$\frac{1}{2}$ ounce tea tree essential oil

1 ounce ground white pumice to be added after you add the tea tree essential oil at the end of soapmaking

Tea Tree

Tea Tree is more scented than Sand Bar

$\frac{1}{2}$ ounce tea tree essential oil

$\frac{1}{2}$ ounce lavender essential oil

$\frac{3}{8}$ ounce ylang ylang essential oil

1 ounce ground white pumice to be added after you add the essential oils at the end of soapmaking

Hula

Hula is the best for getting the sand and sunscreen off after the beach

4 ounces cornmeal

1 teaspoon ground turmeric

½ to ¾ ounce dried calendula flowers, removing the chunky centers (use them for something else) and retaining mostly petals for the soap

$5/8$ ounce tangerine essential oil

$5/8$ ounce ylang ylang essential oil

$1/8$ ounce bergamot essential oil

At the end of soapmaking, add the cornmeal, turmeric and flowers into the soap after you have stirred it, and then add the essential oils. Note that the cornmeal/calendula combo will eventually cause this soap to mold. Try to use it within six months. If you see visible mold, do not use.

SIXTEEN

LIQUID CASTILE SOAP

REMEMBER the Signature Recipe for 100% extra virgin olive oil soap? You can turn it into your own liquid castile soap very easily! Here's how:

Grate one bar of 100% extra virgin olive oil soap, preferably unscented, but smooth (meaning no exfoliating material) at a minimum.

Put the shreds into a sixteen ounce mason jar and put the jar on top of a hot pad or trivet.

Boil two cups of distilled water and pour over the soap shreds. Put a lid on the jar and walk away without disturbing the contents for ten minutes.

Come back and stir vigorously until the soap is dissolved. If you need to thicken it up a bit, dissolve ½ ounce table salt in 1 ½ ounces heated distilled water. Add just a little at a time to avoid over-thickening your soap.

Once the soap has cooled, you can stir in essential oils as desired. Most essential oils do not smell very strong, however, in this soap.

Since we are making it clean and not using any preservatives, this is best made in small batches for immediate use and I like to add twenty drops of tea tree essential oil.

Alternatively, you can purchase Brambleberry's "Natural Castile Liquid Soap Base" in up to a five-gallon-bucket size. Confirm that the ingredients are just: water, olive oil, glycerin and potassium hydroxide. I like the ingredient list, and they claim an impressive shelf life of two years. It's ready for use as-is, or you can thicken it with the saltwater solution.

Packaging

SKS sells both foaming pumps and lotion pumps if you need to source packaging at www.sks-bottle.com.

Face Wash

To make face wash, using an eight ounce pump as your container, add 8 drops tea tree essential oil, 8 drops bergamot essential oil, and 8 drops jojoba to 8 ounces liquid castile soap that has not yet been mixed with any other essential oils. Consider using a foaming pump for your face wash if you'd like. Stir about thirty seconds to mix.

Lighthouse Lemongrass

This is my favorite kitchen sink liquid soap. Using an eight ounce pump as your container, add 8 drops tea tree essential oil and 8 drops lemongrass essential oil to 8 ounces liquid castile soap that has not yet been mixed with any other essential oils. Stir about thirty seconds to mix.

Shaman

This is my favorite for sensitive skin. Using an eight ounce pump as your container, add 3 drops tea tree essential oil and 12 drops lavender essential oil to 8 ounces liquid castile soap that has not yet been mixed with any other essential oils. Stir about thirty seconds to mix.

Baby

Using an eight ounce pump as your container, add 6 drops lavender essential oil to 8 ounces liquid castile soap that has not yet been mixed with any other essential oils. Stir about thirty seconds to mix.

Surf

This makes an invigorating body-wash. Using an eight ounce pump as your container, add 5 drops peppermint essential oil, 3 drops rosemary essential oil and 8 drops spearmint essential oil to 8 ounces liquid castile soap that has not yet been mixed with any other essential oils. Stir about thirty seconds to mix.

SEVENTEEN

ADVANCED SOAP CUTTING

IF YOU WOULD LIKE to transform a loaf of soap into a bunch of smaller soaps, whether to use as gifts, favors or for hospitality, put your geometry skills to work and customize your hand cuts.

This information is for a soap loaf made using an approximately five-pound mold and liner. If you are handy, you can buy reusable silicone five-pound liners from Brambleberry, then fashion your own compatible wooden mold.

Although you can cut soap with a kitchen knife, it is easier to work with the straight or crinkle cutters available through Brambleberry.

But if this is something you need to do regularly, you may wish to invest in specialized cutting equipment like Brambleberry's multi-bar cutter and wire soap slicer to make fifteen full bars or even sixty small bars from one soap loaf. Here is how you can use this special cutting equipment to make sixty small bars with relative ease:

TAKE the soap loaf out of the mold.

ROTATE it onto its side so that the rough part is sideways, not on top.

POSITION THE WIRE soap slicer to bisect the loaf in half the long way, as if you were slicing a freshly made baguette the long way to use it for a giant sandwich. Note: to make this cut almost perfectly even, I work directly on the slicer without using the separate pad piece.

CAREFULLY SLICE the loaf in half the long way, then separate the halves.

TAKING JUST ONE HALF FIRST, position it on the multi bar cutter and slice it; the extra piece will fall off, just set it aside for now.

KEEPING THE SOAP TOGETHER, carefully remove it from the multi bar cutter and set aside.

. . .

RAISE THE CUTTING BAR, then return the cut soap to the multi bar cutter, but position it so that when you bring the cutting bar down the wires will now land so that they cut the bars in half.

CAREFULLY SLICE the bars and remove them from the cutter.

REPEAT these steps with the first remainder piece, the second half, and the second remainder piece.

CONGRATULATIONS, you now should have sixty small bars, plus ends.

THINK about how best to communicate the ingredients in the soap to your recipients. I liked to use small muslin drawstring bags tied to hole-punched postcards that included a lovely visual, description and the ingredients.

EIGHTEEN

SCALING UP

IF YOU HAVE a large family or are making soap to sell, you can scale everything up to be more productive with your time.

All of the soap ingredients must be exactly tripled, and you will need to oversize your equipment and make sure you have enough soap molds and liners.

An organic vapor respirator (OV) is essential for mixing a triple batch of lye, along with a four-cup glass measure to hold the lye crystals and an eight-cup glass measure to hold the distilled water.

Instead of a standard crockpot, use a 20+ quart electric turkey roaster. To avoid scratching the finish of the roasting insert, I recommend a plastic stick blender. And be sure that you are tripling (not doubling) because it is actually safer to blend a triple quantity than a double, which can be shallow and splashy, when using a turkey roaster. Just like you use the low setting on a crockpot, use the top of the "keep warm" area, about 190 degrees Fahrenheit.

The soap will take about the same length of time to saponify as when using a standard crockpot.

You may want to slip the respirator back on when you are mixing in the essential oils as they can be overwhelming in triplicate, particularly a triple batch of Surf.

If you're feeling ambitious, you can also potentially turn one giant batch of soap into three different varieties. After you have removed the turkey roaster insert, give the soap a good stir to release heat, then place $1/3$ into a separate heat proof bowl, and another $1/3$ into another heat proof bowl. You would then add the amount of essential oil that you would use for a single batch into each of the three bowls.

PART THREE

NINETEEN

THEMED PRODUCTION MENUS

AS YOU BEGIN to build up your soap, skincare and body-care pantry, you can organize a themed production day kind of like how you would prepare for a feast day of cooking. Basically you decide what you will make, gather the equipment, ingredients and packaging that you will need ahead of time, then methodically work through your production. If you are making soap, plan to get the soap on first, then make the other items while it is cooking.

Unscented

If you are formulating for someone who is fragrance sensitive to the point of not even wanting anything scented with essential oils, consider this menu, which should take about three hours start-to-finish. You will not be using any essential oils.

- Make Castile Soap and do not add any essential oils to your soap
- While soap is cooking, make Signature Lip Balm Recipe #1
- While Lip Balm is solidifying, make Nourish Serum
- When soap is ready, simply mix it thoroughly and place it in the mold

Well-Being

If self care is on your mind, whether for yourself, family or friends, this is a very fun menu and you can probably do it in about two hours.

- Make Lavender Lip Balm
- While Lip Balm is solidifying, make Lavender, Dream & Rose Geranium Rollers
- Then make Dream spray and Rose Geranium spray
- Remember to label your creations so that you can tell them apart

Eczema/Acne

This menu takes about three hours start-to-finish because the shea butter soap saponifies rather quickly.

- Make Shaman or Char soap

- While soap is cooking, make Shaman Super Sticks, Heel Cream or both
- While balm is solidifying, make Shaman Facial Toner
- When soap is ready, simply add your essential oils as usual and place it in the mold

Mature/Sensitive

This skincare menu takes about two hours start-to-finish and is a real treat!

- Make Frankincense Body & Facial Oil
- Make Frankincense Serum
- Make Frankincense Toner
- Make Frankincense Facial Scrub
- Remember to label your creations so that you can tell them apart

Great Outdoors

This menu takes about three hours start-to-finish. It is a great combination of the items that made up the extremely popular 'bug magnet special.' Remember that you will need room temperature coffee brewed with distilled water for this soap. From the time the coffee is ready for use, this will take about three hours start-to-finish.

- Make Lighthouse Lemongrass Soap

- While soap is cooking, make Shaman Super Sticks
- While sticks are solidifying, make Lighthouse Lemongrass Spray
- When soap is ready, simply add your essential oils as usual and place it in the mold

TWENTY

CUSTOM FORMULATIONS & DILUTION

YOU CAN CUSTOMIZE all of the Signature Recipes in this book to your liking, keeping a few things in mind.

First, research the essential oils that you want to use. If for lip balm, is it considered lip safe? Brambleberry can usually answer that question.

Other great sources of info are the Mountain Rose Herbs blog, Eden Botanicals website, Tisserand Institute website, and the books for further reading listed in the next chapter.

Second, and this is critical, be sure to formulate in an appropriate dilution for your situation. Generally speaking, an appropriate dilution range for adults for bath and body is from 1% to 4% and a good dilution range for facial items is from .2% to 1.5%.

The Tisserand Institute is an excellent source for safety information on dilution. Find topical use and dilution guidelines, as well as dilution ranges for children here:

https://tisserandinstitute.org/safety-guidelines/

Also, you can find an excellent chart for adults here: https://tisserandinstitute.org/essential-oil-dilution-chart/

By way of example, here are the approximate dilution amounts when formulating a two-ounce item, with the number of essential oil drops rounded to whole drops:

2 OUNCE DILUTION

.5% = 8 drops

1% = 18 drops

2% = 36 drops

3% = 54 drops

4% = 72 drops

5% = 90 drops

HERE IS ANOTHER EXAMPLE, this time for 10ml, like the roller recipes.

10ML DILUTION

.5% = 1 drop

1% = 3 drops

2% = 6 drops

3% = 9 drops

4% = 12 drops

5% = 15 drops

Customize Your Soap

If you can dream it, you can do it!

Once you are comfortable with the signature recipes, you are in a great position to customize the scent and texture to your preferences. As you start dreaming, note the following:

Some essential oils smell stronger, longer in soap, like lemongrass, peppermint and spearmint; these are typically the *top notes* of the scent, or the part of the scent you smell right away. The *middle notes* come next, and make up the body of the blend. Examples include tea tree, clary sage and rose geranium. The *base notes* come last as the bottom note of the aroma. Patchouli, sandalwood and vetiver are classic base notes.

Some essential oils carry an enhanced risk of potentially irritating the skin, like eucalyptus and cinnamon. I recommend up to ½-ounce eucalyptus maximum and to avoid using cinnamon essential oil in soap. Instead, consider just a half-teaspoon of ground cinnamon, added at the end of soap-making along with your essential oils.

Clove is another tricky essential oil; it is so powerful that it can potentially reverse saponification at the right temperature. If using clove, be sure that you give your soap a very good stir to release the heat before you add your essential oils.

Depending on what you are going for, use more or less essential oil in your soap. For example, just $^3/_8$-ounce tea tree is perfect for a simple acne bar. But if you are going for more scent, shoot for between about 1 and 1 ½-ounces total essential oil per batch. Then you can adjust a bit up or down to personal preference in future batches. Clary sage essential oil has a lot of interesting properties, including an ability to act as a natural fixative regarding scent. Consider including $^1/_8$-ounce if you are trying to boost the staying power of more elusive scents.

Before you commit to using 1+ ounces of essential oil in your soap, you can dropper onto a cotton round in the rough proportion you are thinking about for the soap and make sure that you like it. For example, if you're thinking about using four different essential oils in equal amounts, that's just one drop each onto the cotton round. You can also formulate your possible blend as a spray or roller using much less essential oil to get more of a sense of it.

If you're thinking of including any botanicals, like lavender buds or calendula petals, understand that the soap must then be used within about six months to avoid mold growth. Otherwise, if you store your soap in a dry, climate-controlled location out of direct sunlight, it can age like fine wine over years!

Importantly, if you wish to vary the ingredients other than essential oils and exfoliating matter, it is very important to run your proposed recipe through a lye calculator to make sure that your fat-to-lye ratio is correct for success. You can find a lye calculator on the Brambleberry website. My suggestion would be to plug in a super fat percentage around five percent. This relates to how much extra fat is in the soap to ensure that all of the lye rearranges itself into soap and glycerin.

TWENTY-ONE

RESOURCES

SOMETIMES THE ARRAY of information can feel over-whelming. My guidance is to try to keep things simple, tune in to your intuition and trust yourself. If something is not resonating with you, avoid it. Let your feelings guide you on your journey.

Although this book is near its end, here are some final guiding thoughts and resources to help you on your journey.

Labeling

It is always a good idea to label what you make. And if you ever plan to offer items for sale, you should always identify each ingredient. An excellent practice is the INCI name followed by the common name in parentheses. INCI stands for *inciterminology* and is the technical, legal, often botanical, name of an ingredient. Wholesale Supplies Plus has on its website a free chart listing INCI terms and Common Names here:

https://www.wholesalesuppliesplus.com/PDFS/INCITerms.pdf

https://www.wholesalesuppliesplus.com/PDFs/INCItoCommonName.pdf

For many years, I printed labels at home using word processing software, photos and a photo printer, and found what I needed at a reasonable price from www.onlinelabels.com.

Eventually I upgraded to professionally designed and printed oil proof and waterproof labels from Lightning Labels at www.lightninglabels.com. My sister Ali Carlucci used graphic design software for these labels.

Ingredients

Sourcing ingredients is part of the fun. Where I have had a strong supplier preference, I have so indicated in the recipes.

A wonderful source for essential oils in sample sizes and loaded with information is Eden Botanicals at www.edenbotanicals.com.

I also adore Mountain Rose Herbs at www.mountainroseherbs.com.

When you need essential oils in larger quantities as in for soapmaking, Brambleberry is excellent.

When sourcing frankincense, my preferred variety is *Boswellia carteri*, however I encourage you to learn about and experiment with all strains.

Another possible ingredient supplier is Bulk Apothecary at www.bulkapothecary.com.

Online Classes

If you would like to see the techniques in this book demonstrated, I offer classes through Hollow Daze U at www. hollowdazeu.com.

For Further Reading

These are my favorite reference books:

Essential Oil Safety: A Guide for Healthcare Professionals by Robert Tisserand and Rodney Young

The Essential Oils Book: Creating Personal Blends for Mind & Body by Colleen K. Dodt

Herbal Recipes for Vibrant Health by Rosemary Gladstar

The Natural Soap Book by Susan Miller Cavitch

The Soapmaker's Companion by Susan Miller Cavitch

These are my favorite adult fiction books involving scent:

Jitterbug Perfume by Tom Robbins

The Scent Keeper by Erica Bauermeister

Thank you Reader. Wishing you health, happiness and success on your formulating journey.

ACKNOWLEDGMENTS

I have so many people to thank in connection with the decade long business that was Hollow Daze Surf Designs—my family, customers, fellow artists, organizers of all of the farmers markets and art shows in which I participated and the retailers who carried my products. As I try to wrap my mind around the scope of this, it brings me happy tears.

With gratitude and thanks to everyone who offered me suggestions and feedback, placed custom orders, and the muses who inspired me to go on to create bestselling items, especially Carloyn Williams, Ali Carlucci, Yessenia Austin, Lynn Anne Madory, Denise Kozer, Grace Stapleton and Denise Turner.

With love and thanks to all of the Hollow Daze super fans who supported me in exactly the right ways at the right times, especially Marie Read, Kathy Bennet, Kathy Berry, Fred Falchook, Bailey Frumen, Cindy and Cassidy Reed,

Jody Sloan, Nikki and Jake Sacks, Bonnie Tolson and Jesse Rast, Kelly Jones, Christina Waggett, Sharon Schisler, Joni Gray, Jennifer Kemp, Katie Forehand, Sheila and family and Anne-Pier and family and all of the librarians in Dare County. I smile every time I think of all of you.

For those who joined me in the early days of Hollow Daze U as I stepped into the role of teacher, I am deeply grateful: Renee O'Neal-Taboada, Julia McPherson, Linda Zirnheld, Susan Joseph, Jennifer Evans, Karen Macdonald, Lyann Abrams and Michelle Robertson. Thank you to Naomi Rhodes and the librarians at the Kill Devil Hills branch of the Dare County Library for inviting me to teach a class for the adult enrichment series and Karen Bachman for spreading the word with her yogis.

Thank you to my farmers market and art show neighbors who were more like extended family, especially Chris Carroll, Stacy Midgett, Denise Turner, Karen Brown, Carolina Coto, Kathleen Redman, Patrick Scheg and Mark Slagle.

Thank you to the gardeners, harvesters, and passionate producers, particularly Donna Griffin, Amanda Dancks, Shaena and Brian McMahon, Chris Carroll, Matt Stankavich and Elizabeth Anderson.

Thank you to my fellow show organizers, particularly Marie Read, Kim Twiddy, Amy Hinnant, Alison Urbanek, Sandy and Dave Briggman, Randi and Blake O'Sullivan, Pete Lewando, Dawn Moraga, Margaret Miller, Trish Dempsey, Kim Mosher and Kevin McCabe, Patty Zukerowski, Shaena McMahon, Suzanne Stark, Charlotte and Jerry Alexander,

Debi Tucker and James Melvin and Chris Sawin and the folks at the Dare County Arts Council.

With thanks to the farmers market managers: Tim Teeple, Paige Griffin, Susan Alif and Rick Anzolut. All of you exhibited so much grace under pressure in the heat of so many summers.

To those who provided a venue for shows, thank you so much, especially Tina McKenzie and the Outer Banks Brewing Station, Shree' Fulcher and the wonderful souls at Ascension Studio, Sam & Omie's, Leanne Robinson and her crew at Secret Spot Surf Shop, Karla Hutchins and the folks at Country Deli, and Karen and company at Goombays.

Thank you Vanessa Trant for setting up a soapmaking book display so many winters ago in the Hatteras Village library. It completely drew me in and launched so many new chapters. I still use the enamel pot that you gave me way back when to melt my solid butters.

Hollow Daze Surf Designs truly was a family affair. Tremendous thanks and love to my husband and business partner Mike, daughter Charlotte, mother Joann, father Nick, sister Ali, brother-in-law Owen, nephew Fin, aunts Nancy, Susan, Linda and great aunt Jean. Your presence at events made them so very special. Thank you with all my heart.

Looking back on this, Hollow Daze Surf Designs touched so many lives during what I now recognize as a golden era of large gatherings. History will judge the actions of the governmental officials who destroyed so many small retail business, like Hollow Daze Surf Designs, in 2020.

Beginning in the Spring of 2021, I hope you'll join me for

classes at hollowdazeu.com. It is my wish that by sharing knowledge, you will learn to make clean soap, skincare and body-care from scratch and ultimately channel your new skills into creating your own custom formulations.

Thank you so much for joining me on our journey. Happy formulating!

ABOUT THE AUTHOR

Christina Deneka spent about a decade formulating 25,000+ clean personal care items in connection with Hollow Daze Surf Designs, a family business in North Carolina's Outer Banks. She is now dedicated to sharing her formerly secret recipes, formulating and soapmaking knowledge with the world through her educational venture Hollow Daze U.

Before moving to coastal North Carolina, forming Hollow Daze with her husband, and learning about essential oils, aromatherapy and herbalism, Christina was an attorney in northern New Jersey, where she led a mostly unscented life due to extreme fragrance sensitivity.

Christina lives on remote Hatteras Island with her husband, daughter, three ducks and a turtle. She is also the author of *Song of the Silver Stallion* published under the pen name C.L. Nectar.

Connect with her at hollowdazeu.com.

Made in the USA
Columbia, SC
19 April 2021